Mills & Boon

A chance to read and collect some of the best-loved novels
from Mills & Boon — the world's largest publisher of romantic
fiction.

Every month, four titles by favourite Mills & Boon authors
will be re-published in the *Classics* series.

A list of other titles in the *Classics* series can be found at the
end of this book.

Anne Mather

THE ARROGANCE
OF LOVE

MILLS & BOON LIMITED
LONDON · TORONTO

First published 1968 by Robert Hale Ltd.
Australian copyright 1980
Philippine copyright 1980
This edition 1980

© Anne Mather 1968

ISBN 0 263 73394 7

Set in 10 on 11 pt. Monotype Baskerville

*Made and printed in Great Britain by
Richard Clay (The Chaucer Press) Ltd,
Bungay, Suffolk*

CHAPTER ONE

SUSAN looked thoughtfully round the crowded lounge of Amanda Blake's apartment. The cocktail party which had begun at five o'clock showed no signs as yet of breaking up, and already it was six-thirty. She had told her fiancé that she would meet him outside their favourite coffee bar in Chelsea at seven, imagining, foolishly, that she would have time before that to return to the flat, which she shared with a friend in a Chelsea mews, to change. But now she would have to go to meet him as she was in the red velvet pants she was wearing, together with a close-fitting black sweater. Even so, there was no guarantee that she would be on time; Amanda Blake's apartment was in Mayfair, and in the rush-hour traffic on a Friday evening, when everyone who could was leaving the city for the less confining surrounds of the suburbs, the chances of getting a taxi to speed her there were very slight, and she would almost certainly be late. Poor David!

It was all very well, she thought gloomily, being secretary to a famous authoress, but Amanda was apt to forget that Susan had a life of her own, and her working hours often extended late into the evening. Not that Susan often objected. Usually, when they were engrossed upon a new novel of suspense, the kind Amanda Blake was noted for, Susan was as eager as Amanda to get on and discover the plot. But these literary cocktail parties, which always occurred at the publication of a new thriller, had begun to bore Susan, and she was always glad when they were over. Of course, it was exciting meeting the Press and other members of the literary fraternity, but tonight she had wanted to get away early to meet

David Chalmers, and now she felt sure it was going to be one of those evenings when nothing went right.

She had been working for Amanda Blake for five years now, since she was a raw teenager of nineteen, and she enjoyed her work immensely. Since her engagement to David, though, things had become a little difficult. David objected strongly to Amanda monopolizing Susan's time. David was an architect, a very junior partner with a well-known firm here in the city, and they hoped to marry in the coming autumn. Amanda, Susan knew, was dreading that time coming. It would mean Susan leaving her, as David would not permit his wife to work at a job which occupied so many hours, and Amanda would have to initiate a new secretary into her ways. This would not be easy. Susan and she had such a grand relationship, and no other secretary would ever take Susan's place entirely.

Just then Amanda approached her secretary. Amanda Blake was a tall broad woman, in her late forties. Unmarried, she had devoted her life to her work and her novels were very popular, both in this country and overseas, where they were translated into many different languages. Her work was of the kind which appealed to almost anybody and there had been talk recently of film rights and adaptations. Susan thought it all very exciting and knew that after she was married she would miss the world that Amanda moved in.

Of course, with the money she had amassed and a small private income, Amanda could have retired, but she enjoyed writing her thrillers as much as everyone enjoyed reading them and could not imagine life without a current who-dunnit on the go. Her hair, a mousey-grey, was cut short and straight. She wore tweeds whatever the occasion, and horn-rimmed spectacles completed a picture of stern solemnity. Not so, however, was the real Amanda, as Susan had soon found out. Quite contrary to her looks she had an unending fund of good humour

6

and a dry and clever wit which endeared her to the columnists.

'Enjoying yourself, Susan?' she asked now, looking at the half-empty glass of gin and vermouth in Susan's hand. She was very fond of her young assistant and their association veered nearer to a mother-and-daughter relationship than that of employer and employee.

Susan smiled. 'I thought it would have been over by now, Amanda,' she replied, sighing.

'I expect you've got a date with that young man of yours,' remarked Amanda dryly. 'Let him wait. Good for the soul, you know. Absence makes the heart grow fonder and all that.'

Susan laughed. 'You always say that,' she answered. 'And David does quite a bit of waiting for me. What time is this likely to dry up?'

'Sevenish,' said Amanda. 'Will that do?'

Susan opened her mouth to reply when an eager reporter beat her to it and bore Amanda off to discuss some aspect of the new novel.

Sighing again, Susan turned and walked into the large modern kitchen which adjoined the lounge, and poured the remains of her drink down the sink. She had had four gin slings already. She did not want to meet David in an intoxicated condition. He was a teetotaller and disapproved of alcohol.

She drew a pack of cigarettes out of the pocket of her slacks and lit one and then looked critically at her reflection in the mirror above the draining board. Green, sleepy eyes looked back at her, veiled by long black lashes, while her ash-blonde hair hung loosely to her shoulders where it curved up lightly at the ends. Her hair was thick and silky soft, and did not need to curl to be attractive.

Suddenly, she became aware that someone was watching her from the doorway which led to the tradesmen's entrance of the apartment; someone who was very big and broad and darkly attractive, with raven's-wing dark hair which was inclined to curl on his collar. Dressed in a thigh-length overcoat and a dark suit, he was quite the most physically attractive man she had ever seen; he was so completely *male*, and estimating that he was about thirty-five, she imagined she would not be the first, or the last, woman to think so.

Aware of a kind of breathlessness about her, she managed to say: 'Who on earth are you?'

'A newspaper man,' he remarked, non-committally.

Susan flushed beneath his gaze, annoyed at feeling suddenly so inadequate. Being a tall girl herself, she usually was on eye-level terms with the men of her acquaintance. This man dwarfed her, and immediately put her at a disadvantage.

'The . . . the cocktail party guests usually use the front door,' she said, managing to sound cool, though she felt far from it.

He shrugged his broad shoulders and lit a cigar.

'I prefer to see A.B. alone,' he answered smoothly.

Susan ran a tongue over her dry lips. 'Really! And will she want to see you?'

'I think so,' he murmured. 'Amanda and I are old friends. Unfortunately we seldom see anything of each other.'

'Well, if you go through you can see her now,' said Susan, running a nervous hand through her hair.

'I'll wait until the rabble have gone, if you don't mind,' he replied casually. 'I've been abroad for some considerable time, and I'd like to see the old girl alone.'

Susan was shocked. How dare he address Amanda Blake as 'the old girl'? Who was he?

She turned to go intending to tell Amanda immediately that he was here. After all, she only had his word that he knew her employer at all. But he caught her wrist as she passed him and stopped her.

'Don't go,' he murmured. 'Stay and keep me company. How about getting me a drink?'

Susan wrenched her wrist out of his grasp. His touch had sent the blood pounding through her veins, and she realized with horror at her own duplicity that she had enjoyed the feel of those hard fingers gripping her arm.

'If you want a drink, you'll have to go in there for it,' she said angrily.

He grinned. 'If I remember correctly, A.B. used to keep a bottle of Scotch in the cupboard over the refrigerator, for medicinal purposes such as this.'

Susan clenched her fists. She crossed to the cupboard he had mentioned and, sure enough, at the back stood the bottle of Scotch. Really, she thought, he seemed to know an awful lot!

She lifted the bottle out, took a glass from the drainer and poured him a drink. 'Ice?' she queried, in a voice as cold as ice itself.

'Naturally.'

Susan took the tongs and lifted two large pieces of ice out of the ice container and dropped them into the amber liquid. Then she handed him the glass. The man took it, nodding his thanks. Susan stubbed out her cigarette in the near-by ashtray, and he said:

'Won't you join me?'

'No, thanks,' she replied shortly, glancing at her watch. It was almost seven now.

'Got a heavy date?' he asked. 'You're A.B.'s secretary, aren't you?'

'Yes, to both questions,' she answered, acutely conscious of him. She turned to look at him again; she had been avoiding his eyes but suddenly she found her eyes held by his and something seemed to flare in his at the contact. It was fantastic, crazy, and yet she felt drawn to him; something dangerous and exciting and forbidden seemed to be in the room. He must have felt it, too, for his eyes narrowed slightly, and he looked at her through half-closed lids. Susan wondered whether the amount of alcohol she had consumed was clouding her brain. This was all so – so – mad!

She forced herself to look away, and said, breathlessly: 'I must go back.'

All at once the door from the lounge opened and Amanda stood there.

'They've all gone now—' she began, and then stopped in amazement. 'Dominic – Dominic Halstad!'

The man smiled, his eyes dancing, and Amanda rushed across the room and hugged him warmly. Over her shoulder, the man's eyes sought Susan's and she had to steel herself to force things back into perspective.

For, as Amanda made a fuss of the man, chattering volubly, the name she had used caused Susan no little feeling of trepidation.

Dominic Halstad! No ordinary newspaper man as she had assumed. He was the chairman of the board of directors of Halstad Press Limited, one of the largest syndicates of newspapers and magazines in the country.

If she had not felt so strange she would have felt like laughing. And she had thought he was trying to get an inside story! She turned away and lit another cigarette with trembling fingers. Dominic Halstad! *Glory!*

Then Amanda was saying: 'Susan, my dear, come and meet one of my closest and oldest friends, Dominic Halstad. You've heard of him, of course.'

'Of course,' murmured Susan politely, flushing as his firm fingers gripped her hand for a moment and then released it again.

'Miss . . . er . . .?' he began slowly.

'Stacey,' put in Amanda swiftly, 'but I'm sure Susan will do, won't it, darling?'

'Of course,' said Susan, again, feeling rather ridiculous because she could think of nothing else to say.

'Well, Susan has been looking after me,' said Dominic Halstad lazily. He was completely in control of himself, and Susan thought she must have imagined the look in his eyes a moment ago. Which was just as well, she thought dryly. If his name had told her nothing else, it had at least warned her that he was a *married* man.

Amanda smiled. 'Susan's a real treasure,' she said, putting an arm about her secretary's shoulders.

'Of course we didn't introduce ourselves properly,' continued the man mockingly.

Susan felt uncomfortable and as though sensing it, Amanda said:

'You can get along now and meet that young man of yours, Susan.'

'Thank you,' said Susan, with relief. 'Good-bye, Mr. Halstad.'

She hurried out into the living-room where Amanda's maid and general factotum, Sarah, was trying to create order out of the disorder of dirty glasses and overflowing ashtrays that was left.

'G'bye, Sarah,' she called, and, pulling her sheepskin coat about her shoulders, she left the apartment.

She managed eventually to hail a taxi, and giving the address of the coffee bar she sank back against the leather upholstery. Feeling able to relax she found her thoughts turning back to the last few minutes at the apartment and her encounter with Dominic Halstad.

She had treated him like an intruder, and she wondered whether he would tell Amanda how impolite she had been.

He had been attractive though. Susan sighed, and wondered what his wife was like. Although she knew he was married she could not remember ever having read anything about his wife. His name appeared from time to time in the city society magazines, and recently she had read about him in America, but his wife did not seem to accompany him very often.

David was waiting impatiently outside the coffee bar. He was striding up and down, trying to keep warm, for it was a cool March evening. He looked disgustedly at her trews and the sheepskin coat. He did not like to see women in trousers, least of all his fiancée. He was rather old-fashioned, and although at times Susan found it rather endearing, at others it exasperated her.

'Do you realize it's seven-thirty?' he exclaimed, by way of a greeting.

'Yes, darling,' said Susan, in a mock-subdued tone. 'I'm sorry.'

'And I gather, from the way you're dressed, that you haven't been home since this morning.'

'Correct,' she murmured. 'You know I told you that Amanda was having the cocktail party for the new book this afternoon. That's why I'm so late. It's only just broken up.'

David snorted. 'Susan, you're not paid to attend that woman's cocktail parties!'

'I know, David, but she does so like me to be there, and I don't like to disappoint her.'

'It doesn't matter about disappointing me, of course!'

'Oh, David, don't be silly. I haven't disappointed you. I'm here, aren't I? Come on, let's go in, I'm starving!'

'We aren't going in,' he said abruptly. 'Mother has invited us back for supper. She wants to discuss the wedding.'

He ignored the way Susan's face dropped at this news. Susan and Mrs. Chalmers did not get along very well. Mrs. Chalmers was a widow, and David was her only child. Consequently, she was rather possessive and jealously did not want him to marry and leave her. David was tall and slim and fair, and she had brought him up to despise most of the members of her own sex. He did not smoke or drink and attended church with her twice every Sunday.

When he met Susan, one day in the tube (he accidentally sent Susan's shopping flying when he bumped into her), he found all his mother had told him accounted for little against his own attraction for the blonde, green-eyed creature who thanked him so merrily for picking up her parcels.

He could hardly believe his luck the following evening when they again travelled on the same train, and when he asked to see her again she agreed eagerly.

But when he took her home a few weeks later to meet his mother, he found things were not going to be as smooth as he had hoped. Mrs. Chalmers spent the whole evening sulking and Susan could hardly wait to escape from the close confines of Medlar Grove.

As time went by, and Mrs. Chalmers realized that David was not to be swayed from Susan, whatever she said, she tried to be a little more friendly, and finally decided that if David was to marry Susan, she might as well make the best of it. After all, they could nicely live with her after the event. The house was old and large for one person and that way she would be able to keep David under her roof. Things would not be so different after all.

But Susan soon realized the way things were going and lost no time in saying that she and David hoped to be able to save enough money to put a deposit down on a small house in one of the new suburban developments.

Mrs. Chalmers, however, was no defeatist, and still would not accept that David would agree to such a thing and leave his mother alone. Thus it was that David was being pulled two ways, and was not yet strong enough to defy his mother and make a stand.

Susan herself was hoping that he would not allow his

mother to get her own way, as she knew she could never live with Mrs. Chalmers. They were too different, and it would never work out.

Now, Susan merely sighed, and said: 'Oh, all right, David. But I wish you wouldn't spring these things on me. I've been looking forward all day to this evening alone together.'

David relented a little, and replied, 'Never mind, Sue darling, we don't have long to wait and then we'll be together for always.'

'Y . . . e . . . s,' murmured Susan, rather cautiously. Their future had never seemed more insecure. What was wrong with her? Why was she feeling so depressed tonight? It could only be this sudden visit to Medlar Grove. What else was there?

She refused to allow herself to think about that moment in Amanda's kitchen. What was she, that she could allow herself, even for a moment, to respond to the message in another man's eyes? A message which she felt she had imagined anyway.

David ran a small M.G. sports car of almost vintage origin, and they drove in it round to David's home in Shepherd's Bush. Mrs. Chalmers let them in. She must have been watching for them from the window, and Susan shivered at the pictures this conjured up. Pictures of their lives in a few years' time if they lived here. No, it could never be. And if love was involved, she realized with a sense of loss that she did not love David enough to submit to such a life.

When she saw Susan's trousers, Mrs. Chalmers exclaimed, 'Dear me, I hope none of the neighbours saw you come in!'

It was on the tip of Susan's tongue to say that if all the street were like Mrs. Chalmers, there was every chance that she had been seen. But respect for David made her refrain and she simply ignored the remark, and walking into the gloomy living-room warmed her hands at the electric fire.

'Susan didn't have time to change before she came,' said David by way of explanation when Susan did not answer herself.

'Why? You're late enough, aren't you?'

David sighed. 'Susan had to work late.'

'And have you been standing around in the cold waiting for her? You'll catch your death of cold one of these days, mark my words.'

'He's not made of glass, you know,' Susan was stung to reply at last. 'And I couldn't let him know.'

Mrs. Chalmers shrugged and left them for a few minutes to prepare the supper. Susan took off her coat and laid the table while David switched on the television and began to watch a quiz programme.

Susan looked at him and sighed. He was not a very romantic person, and it had never occurred to him that he had not yet kissed her, or told her he was glad to see her. Unless he was prized away from his mother's apron-strings he never would. This atmosphere was cloying. It sapped all original thought. Mrs. Chalmers was in evidence everywhere. From the ridiculous 'Home, Sweet Home' embroidered picture on the wall to the swear box on the mantelpiece.

Supper as usual was a concoction of scrambled eggs and bacon and after it was over Susan defiantly lit a cigarette. She did not smoke a lot, but tonight she felt so restless she had to do something to calm her nerves. She drew the smoke deeply into her lungs and then exhaled with satisfaction.

As usual, the conversation veered to the subject of the wedding. As Susan had no relatives of her own, Mrs. Chalmers had taken over the arrangements herself, and, of the forty guests on the list, only about a dozen were friends of Susan's.

The question of the house was raised, and Mrs. Chalmers again made her point about this house coming to David on her death anyway, and that to buy a new house was quite ridiculous and much too extravagant.

'David doesn't want to be troubled with mortgages at a time like this,' she said severely. 'After all, this house is far too big for one person. And if David leaves I shall be all alone.'

'You could sell it,' Susan remarked quietly.

'What! Sell my home! Then what would I do?'

Suddenly afraid that Mrs. Chalmers, or David for that matter, might suggest that she come to live with them should they buy a new house, Susan said quickly, 'You could afford to buy a smaller house. Or alternatively, you could rent a flat. In fact, a flat would suit you admirably.'

'A flat!' Mrs. Chalmers' face was red. 'I couldn't live in a *flat*!'

'Why not?'

Mrs. Chalmers swallowed hard. 'You wouldn't understand, never having had a home of your own, but a home is something more than three up and two down, you know.'

Susan flushed. It hurt still, when anyone spoke so crudely of her upbringing. Truthfully the orphanage had been a wonderful place, and she still went back there sometimes to see the Matron, but it had not been quite the same as a real home, with a mother and father of her very own. She was sure that this was something else that marred her in David's mother's eyes. She seemed to look down on orphanages, as though the children in them were themselves responsible for their lack of parentage.

David must have felt uncomfortable himself at this, for he suddenly stretched and rose to his feet.

'Well, Sue, it's nearly ten. Shall we be going?'

Gratefully, Susan rose also. 'Oh, yes, David. Can you get my coat?'

Outside, the night air seemed inestimably fresh after the dingy atmosphere of the Chalmers house. Susan breathed deeply and was glad for once that the car was an open one. It was wonderful to feel the cold wind tugging at her hair, and clearing her head.

She wished David was not so easily dominated by his mother. For instance, he never chastened her for anything she said to herself, Susan, whatever it might be, and for all she might think that it was because he wanted to keep the peace she knew this was the coward's way out. Mrs. Chalmers might not be so objectionable if she were taken down a peg or two, now and then.

It was a problem, and she did not have any idea how it was to be solved.

When they drew up outside the block of apartments where Susan's flat was situated, she turned to David and said:

'David, let's get this straight now, shall we? I don't want to live with your mother, however convenient it may be.'

David sighed. 'I know, Sue, but –'

'But nothing, David.' Susan ran a hand over her hair, and David suddenly pulled her to him.

'Oh, Sue,' he whispered, 'I only want to live with you. I don't care where it is!'

Susan allowed him to kiss her, without responding herself. She felt emotionally exhausted at the moment. Then she pressed herself against him, as though willing herself to respond, and he groaned, 'Oh, lord, I don't know how I'll wait until October.'

'What would your mother think?' she taunted him, hating herself for doing so.

'I don't damn well care,' he muttered, and kissed her again.

CHAPTER TWO

THE flat which Susan shared was situated in a comparatively new block in a quiet cul-de-sac. There was a bedroom, a living-room and a kitchen, with a bathroom along the passage which was shared with two other couples.

Delia Fulton and Susan had both been brought up in the orphanage and in consequence loved the flat which was the first real home they had had. They had both come to London together to get jobs, Susan to work in a typing pool and take a commercial course during her evenings, and Delia to work in a large store from where she too had taken a course, this time in window-dressing, and she now worked for a large department store in Oxford Street.

It had been a struggle to begin with. The rent of the flat had seemed exorbitant, but now they both earned enough money to afford the flat and a few luxuries besides.

The girls were good friends and did not interfere in each other's lives. The orphanage had taught them to respect privacy, for there there had been little.

The next morning Susan woke to find Delia shaking her, and saying:

'Wake up, Susan. I've brought you a cuppa.'

Delia was a brunette. She wore her hair very long and straight and was invariably dressed in pants and an overblouse or sweater.

'What's the time?' asked Susan, struggling up in bed to take the cup of tea Delia held out to her.

'Eight o'clock,' replied Delia, now relieved of the teacup and lighting a cigarette.

Susan blinked. This was indeed a red-letter day. Delia

was never up first in the mornings. She was always the one who had practically to push her friend out of bed.

'Couldn't you sleep?' she asked, an amused twinkle in her eye. 'Or is there some other reason for your early rising?'

Delia stretched and grinned. 'Well, honey, Alan is taking me down to meet his parents for the weekend. He's calling for me at nine o'clock and I can hardly contain myself.'

'I see. How wonderful!' Susan was pleased. Alan Huntley was the nephew of the store-manager where Delia worked. His parents were Sir John and Lady Olivia Huntley and they lived in a massive house near Bristol. Although Delia had been working at the store for over eight years, it was only recently that Alan had started taking an interest in her and as she had admired him from a distance for a long time, she was overjoyed. And now he was taking her down to meet his parents and to Susan it sounded very serious indeed in the nicest possible way.

'It is, isn't it?' exclaimed Delia, hugging herself. 'Just imagine! Meeting his parents!'

'Yes, you'll soon be getting married yourself,' said Susan. 'I envy you.'

'Why? You have David.'

'Oh, I know, but I also have David's mother to contend with, and she's a whole mass of problems in herself.' She sighed.

'You do sound gloomy this morning,' said Delia sympathetically. 'You were asleep when I got home last night. Has something awful happened?'

'Awful! Oh, no, not really.' In truth Susan couldn't understand her depressed mood herself. It all seemed to stem from that meeting with Dominic Halstad. It was all most annoying, and most unsettling.

'Then what's wrong? You don't sound very happy.'
Delia was genuinely concerned.

Susan smiled. 'Nothing, honestly. I just feel as though
it's going to be one of *those* days.'

She slid out of bed and stretched, before crossing to the
wash basin to sluice her face with icy cold water.

Drying her face on the towel, she looked speculatively
at Delia.

'Delia,' she said slowly, 'have you heard of Dominic
Halstad?'

Delia frowned. 'I've heard of him, of course. He's
something to do with newspapers, isn't he?'

'Yes. He's the head of one of these big syndicates.'

Delia looked exasperated. 'Come on, then! You didn't
ask me that for no reason, just out of the blue. Do you
know him?' She looked slightly incredulous.

Susan laughed. 'Not exactly. But I did meet him yesterday at the cocktail party at Amanda's. He's a friend
of hers, and very attractive.'

'Is he indeed?' Delia made a moue with her lips. 'You
do move in exalted circles, don't you?'

'Amanda does, at least. She apparently knows him
very well. They treated each other like long-lost souls.'

'Hmn! He sounds interesting. Is he married?'

'Yes, they always are,' Susan chuckled. 'Why? Has
Alan begun to pall already?'

'Of course not. But I can see he made quite an impression on you. Is that the cause of the depression? Did
David seem meek in comparison?'

'No, not at all.' Susan felt cross. She ought not to be
discussing a complete stranger, and a friend of Amanda's,
in this manner. After all, the chances were that she would
never see him again. Besides, she somehow felt disloyal
to David just talking about Dominic Halstad. But she
would not admit, even to herself, the reason why she
felt this way.

Shooing Delia out of the bedroom she dressed in a dark-blue jersey shift and emerged to find that Delia had prepared her a slice of toast and a cup of creamy coffee, which were delicious.

Wishing her friend good luck during the weekend, she donned her sheepskin coat, and hastily left the flat. She ran down the flight of stairs and came out into the fresh morning air.

It was one of those slightly frosty mornings, when a faint haze hid the sun and promised a warm and sunny day. Susan breathed deeply and felt her depression leaving her. Who could feel depressed when everything looked so new and fresh and the young shoots were greening on the trees in the parks?

A bus set her down near Amanda's apartment and she opened the door of the lounge as the near-by church clock struck nine.

Amanda was sitting at her desk, studying her correspondence, and smiled as Susan came in.

'Good morning, Susan,' she said briskly. 'You're remarkably punctual.'

Susan chuckled. 'I'm not sure whether I should take that as a compliment or not,' she remarked, taking off her coat and hanging it in the minute entrance hall.

'Sorry, dear,' said Amanda. 'Anyway, there's not a lot for us to do today.' She rose to her feet and, crossing to the kitchen door, called, 'Coffee for two, Sarah, please.'

Then she turned to Susan. 'There are just a few letters to answer, and afterwards I think we'll take a ride into the country. It will make a nice change for both of us.'

While they were smoking cigarettes and drinking some of the continental coffee Sarah had prepared so expertly, Amanda said, 'By the way, what did you think of Dominic Halstad?'

'I don't really know,' replied Susan, flushing. 'He . . . well . . . he didn't tell me who he was, and I'm afraid I was rather abrupt with him. I treated him like an eager reporter trying to get an inside story.'

Amanda laughed. 'Oh, don't worry about that. I expect he was quite amused. He's used to people hanging on his every word. Do him good to meet someone who didn't treat him like the purple emperor.'

'He did say he was a very good friend of yours.'

'So he is, girl.' Amanda nodded thoughtfully. 'You know it was he who persuaded his father to publish my first novel. They weren't very inspiring stories in those days, but Dominic thought I had promise and persuaded his father to think so, too. Of course, I've known Dominic for years. Long before I took up writing, in fact. His mother and mine were great friends, and when we were children we used to play together. I was seven years older than Dom, but he led me a terrible life.' She chuckled reminiscently.

'I see.' That accounted for the familiar way he had spoken of her. 'He hasn't been here before, has he?'

'No, he's been abroad for quite a long time,' replied Amanda. 'He seems to do a lot of his work in America, or so I believe; at any rate I haven't seen him for a couple of years or so.'

'He seems very young,' commented Susan, drawing deeply on her cigarette. 'But he must be nearly forty.'

'He is, darling. But I agree, he doesn't look his age, which is remarkable in the circumstances.'

'What circumstances?' Susan was curious.

'Oh, the problems he has had to face with Veronica.'

'Veronica? Oh, is she his wife?'

'That's right.' Amanda sounded bitter. 'Regrettably.'

Susan stubbed out her cigarette. 'Why so? Are they divorced?'

'No. Nothing so simple.' She smiled, a little forcedly, and then said, 'Well, let's get on.'

Susan picked up her notebook, but as she did so she

wondered why Amanda seemed so reluctant to talk about Dominic Halstad's wife. There seemed to be a mystery about the whole affair, but she respected Amanda's confidence and firmly tried to push all thoughts of the Halstad *ménage* from her mind.

But it was not so easy as she thought, and she found her mind twisting back over all that had been said, trying to find some reason for Amanda's oblique comments.

But it was no use. She did not know sufficient about them to be able to form any opinion, and it seemed unlikely that Dominic Halstad should have any problems that he could not handle, when she considered his immense wealth and personal charm.

They lunched at the apartment and afterwards drove out of town in Amanda's Rolls-Royce, Susan acting as chauffeuse. They stopped at a small country pub for a drink, and relaxed in the garden of the inn, sitting at rustic tables on wooden forms.

It was all very olde-worlde and Susan liked it.

'I'm having dinner with Dominic this evening,' remarked Amanda suddenly. 'At least, I should say he's having dinner with me. He's coming to the apartment.'

'Alone?' Susan was intrigued. Where was his wife?

'Yes. Alone. Why? Would you and David like to make up a foursome?'

'Oh, really . . . I . . . of course we wouldn't intrude . . .' Susan felt embarrassed.

'You wouldn't be intruding,' replied Amanda easily. 'It's a grand idea. Why didn't I think of it before?'

Susan's nerves felt as taut as violin strings, and she inwardly rated herself for feeling this way at the mere mention of that man's name.

'I don't think David would want to come,' she explained truthfully.

'Oh, never mind what that young man says. Would you like to come?'

'I . . . I suppose so.'

Amanda screwed her nose up, and looked rather cynical. 'I must say your enthusiasm is overwhelming,' she remarked dryly.

Susan giggled. 'I'm sorry, Amanda. Of course, I'd like to come, but you know what David is.'

'I know,' said Amanda. 'Why don't you give him a ring? I expect he'll be working as usual today, won't he? Tell him Dom is coming. I guarantee he won't refuse.'

'Perhaps you're right,' agreed Susan, sighing. 'All right. I'll go and see if I can use the phone here.'

The bartender was quite willing that she should use the phone behind the bar and in no time at all her call was ringing in David's office. Although occasionally she did contact David in this way, it was only very occasionally as he did not like her ringing him during office hours. Thus it was that when David answered and found it was Susan he was rather irritable.

'What is it?' he asked brusquely. 'I'm very busy, Susan. Is it urgent?'

'Not exactly, darling, but Amanda has invited us to the apartment for dinner this evening and I didn't want to accept until I was sure you would want to go.'

'I see.' David did not sound enthusiastic, but, thought Susan impatiently, he expected her to visit his mother's whenever he saw fit, so why should he object on the rare occasions when she asked him to go somewhere that she wanted? After all, Amanda was the nearest person to a mother she was ever likely to have.

'It will make a change,' she said, annoyed to find that her voice was persuasive. 'Will you go?'

David hesitated and then said, 'Do I take it Amanda will be alone? Or will there be other guests?'

'One other guest, Dominic Halstad,' said Susan quickly.

24

'Dominic Halstad!' David sounded astonished now. 'Really?'

'Yes, really.' Susan felt angry. As Amanda had said, the name had caused an immediate and favourable reaction.

'Well, in that case, I think we might go. It sounds interesting. Is he a friend of Amanda's?'

'Yes. Right. What time will you pick me up?'

Susan was glad when she replaced the receiver. She had been conscious of having the attention of the bartender while she was making the call and she hoped she had not sounded too pleading. Thanking him, she returned to Amanda.

'Well?' said Amanda at once. 'What's the verdict?'

'As soon as I mentioned Mr. Halstad's name, it worked like a charm.' Susan sighed. 'I don't know why you and David are so antipathetic to one another.'

The last time David and Susan had dined at the apartment, Amanda and David had spent the whole evening arguing over contemporary painting. Amanda was a devotee of modern art, whereas David could not stand it and, unlike Amanda, he did not think everyone should have their own opinion. He had inherited from his mother the idea that he was right and everyone else must be wrong.

'That young man annoys me,' said Amanda, 'and he knows it. He is also jealous of my monopolizing your time. Are all young men today so sure of themselves?'

'Being sure of himself is the last description I would have applied to David,' said Susan in surprise. 'With me he seems anything but positive. He allows his mother to walk all over him, and me too for that matter. It's infuriating.'

'Well, I should imagine that's why he is the way he is,' remarked Amanda. 'At home he's been repressed and dominated by his mother, that's why when he's with you he tries to dominate you. To prove to himself that he's not a mouse.'

Susan laughed. 'The amateur psychiatrist, Miss Amanda Blake!'

Amanda grinned. 'All right, all right, you laugh. But I'm right. I'm sure of it. What happened to his father?'

'Oh, he died years ago.'

'Probably bullied to death, if you ask me,' said Amanda shrewdly. 'From what you've said, his mother sounds a tyrant.'

Susan sighed. 'Maybe it's my fault. I let her get away with too much. I think that's David's dilemma too. After his father died she turned to him more and more and consequently today things are worse than ever. She needs a daughter-in-law who is as tough as she is and who will answer her back and not allow her to get her own way.'

Amanda frowned. 'That was an ambiguous remark. Do I take it you're having doubts as to whether you'll be her daughter-in-law?'

Susan flushed. 'Oh, no! No!' She lit a cigarette hastily, with hands that were not quite steady. 'It's just that sometimes I wish I were more like that.'

'Is that so?' Amanda looked sceptical, and Susan wondered whether the remark she had made had indeed been triggered by some subconscious desire to be free of the Chalmers family once and for all.

But, she told herself desperately, she did love David, and that was all that mattered. Once they were married she would feel differently about everything. Once they were settled in a home of their own, and perhaps with a family, too, she would find her fears had merely been will-o'-the-wisps, without any substance or foundation. For once she was married to David, she felt sure she would be able to handle his mother in a more positive way.

That evening she dressed with care for their dinner

26

engagement. She wore a dress of heavy black silk which clung to the slender lines of her figure, revealing the curve of her breast and the lithe smoothness of her hips. With it she wore a dark red cape and she was ready and waiting when David arrived at seven-fifteen. He, too, looked smart in a dinner jacket and Susan wondered what he had told his mother about this evening.

He looked very impressed when he saw Susan and said, 'I'm quite looking forward to this evening. Halstad is a very influential man. He may be able to put some work our way.'

Susan stared at him. 'What on earth has a pressman in common with an architect?'

'Well, nothing really, my dear, but Halstad doesn't only dabble in things literary. He has interests all over the world. Why, Mathews was only saying this afternoon what an opportunity this was . . .'

Susan gasped. Mathews was the head partner in the firm and a man she both disliked and despised. A married man, he spent his free time at night clubs and strip-shows, taking up with different women to the shame and embarrassment of his wife, caring nothing for his three children, other than that they be provided with a paid education and adequately provided with the material comforts his money could buy. On the rare occasions when he had encountered Susan he had treated her like another of his conquests and she had been horrified that David had done nothing and said nothing to prevent her discomfort.

'If you think this evening is going to be turned into a business meeting, you're mistaken,' she exclaimed hotly. 'Amanda has invited us and you will kindly remember that and give her the consideration she deserves. I will not have you introducing work into the conversation. Good heavens, Dominic Halstad isn't interested in Mathews, Mathews, Graham and *Chalmers*!'

David looked taken aback. 'I say, Susan, don't get on your high horse, old girl. I'm only thinking of us, you know.'

'Are you? Are you?' Susan buttoned her cape. 'Anyway, remember what I've said, and try to be a little more friendly towards Amanda. She's been very kind to me, and I'm very fond of her.'

'All right, Susan, I get the message,' said David, becoming a little annoyed now. 'I don't know why you think I would say anything out of place. I'm sure I have as much discretion as the next man.'

Susan smiled at this and wished wryly that it was true.

They arrived at Amanda's apartment at about seven-forty-five. Sarah admitted them and they removed their coats in the hallway before entering the large lounge.

This room extended the length of the apartment block and was divided by a librenza into two parts; one used for dining and the other as the lounge. It was tastefully decorated with furniture which was neither modern nor old-fashioned. Amanda was not interested in collectors' items and yet there were several good pieces of Sheraton and Chippendale which looked rather out of place beside the Formica-topped occasional table and stereophonic radiogram.

Dominic Halstad was seated on the low couch near the pseudo-log fire, the diffused lighting darkening his already tanned skin and giving him a faintly foreign air. He was sitting forward glancing at the draft of Amanda's latest novel, and he looked at home and very relaxed.

He rose to his feet immediately at their entrance, and smiled. Susan was acutely aware of how her nerves had tensed again, and of how her spine tingled in a most unusual manner. The colour mounted in her cheeks and she was glad that David's eyes were not on her at that moment.

But David himself was walking towards the other man,

holding out his hand and saying, 'You must be Mr. Halstad. My name is Chalmers, sir. I'm very pleased to meet you.'

Feeling she was neglecting her duties, Susan hastily joined them and made unnecessary introductions. She felt aware that Dominic Halstad was rather amused by her, and she felt annoyed and altogether uncomfortable.

After they were seated, Dominic said, 'Amanda is fussing over the dinner in the kitchen, so can I provide you with a drink? What would you like, Susan?'

Susan shrugged. 'A Martini, perhaps,' she murmured. 'Thank you.'

'How about you, Chalmers?'

David bit his lip. 'I . . . well . . . perhaps the same for me, sir.'

Dominic raised his dark eyebrows and walked indolently across to the cocktail cabinet. Susan glanced at David and he shrugged his shoulders defensively. He had never accepted a drink in her presence before.

Dominic returned with two Martinis and a Scotch with ice for himself. After handing them their drinks he seated himself opposite them in a low armchair and said:

'I understand you're engaged. When do you intend getting married?'

'In October,' replied David swiftly. 'We're saving up for a house.'

Susan glanced at David. So they *were* going to have their own house. She wondered whether he had told his mother so definitely. It did not seem likely. It was probably simply bravado away from her domineering attitude.

'Very good. There are some pleasant new developments on the outskirts of the city. I've noticed quite a number of changes since my return.'

'You've been abroad?' David was interested.

'Yes. I only returned this week.'

29

'Really. Where have you been?'

Susan glanced at the kitchen door, and wondered whether she could make some excuse and go and talk to Amanda in the kitchen. For some reason, Dominic Halstad's presence overpowered her and she found she could not look away from his compelling gaze.

Amanda emerged from the kitchen at that moment, as though in answer to Susan's unspoken prayer, and said:

'Hullo, there. How are you, David?' She smiled round. 'I see you've all been provided with drinks. Good. I thought Dom would look after you.'

The two men, who had risen at her entrance, reseated themselves as Amanda took the chair beside Susan. Then Dominic got up again, and grinned.

'I suppose I ought to offer you a drink,' he remarked laughingly. 'After all, it's your apartment and your liquor.'

'That's right, darling. I'll have a whisky, please, with a little ginger.'

David looked disapprovingly at Susan, and she shrugged almost imperceptibly. Martinis were one thing. Strong stuff like Scotch was for men, not for women!

They lit cigarettes, although Dominic Halstad produced a case of cigars and preferred to have one of them. David refused a cigarette but accepted a cigar, and Susan felt an uncontrollable fit of giggles assailing her. Surely David, who did not smoke, was not going to attempt to smoke a cigar!

But David allowed Dominic Halstad to light his cigar and drew back, puffing furiously.

Susan looked away from him, and turned to Amanda in order to stop herself from laughing, while Dominic Halstad lay back in his seat, an amused expression on his face.

Susan felt suddenly annoyed with him. Did he know

how inexperienced David was at smoking? Had Amanda told him he was both a teetotaller and a non-smoker? If he did know, he was being deliberately provocative. Amanda, apparently unconcerned, said, 'How's Jon these days?'

'He's fine, thanks. He's looking forward to seeing you. I told him I would bring him to lunch with you some time next week. I'm sending him to Fay's in a few days. He can stay there for a week or so. I know he doesn't like going, but it will do him good to get with children of his own age. He's far too precocious. That's what comes of always being with adults.'

Susan listened to this conversation with interest. Who was Jon? Her question was soon answered as Amanda said, by way of explanation:

'Jon is Dominic's son. He's fifteen, and he lives in England most of the time. Dom doesn't take him with him on his travels, do you, Dom?'

Dominic's eyes narrowed. 'Unfortunately not. I feel I'm neglecting him at times, but at others I realize that were we together more we would probably get in each other's way.'

Susan looked aghast. 'What a thing to say!' she exclaimed, before she could stop herself. 'Poor boy!'

Dominic's eyes were mocking. 'There's nothing poor about Jon, believe me,' he remarked coolly. He looked at Amanda. 'Is there, A.B.?'

'No, I suppose not. But I can understand Susan's feelings. She has never known a parent's love; she was brought up in an orphanage. To hear you speak of Jon you would imagine he was an encumbrance to you.'

Dominic sighed, and drew deeply on his cigar. 'Let's say Jon and I are too much alike to get along well together,' he remarked. 'We both like our own way too much.'

'Besides,' said Amanda dryly, 'the kind of life you lead is not fitting for a child of that age.'

David, who had not been taking any part in this conversation, looked appalled at Amanda's candid manner of speaking. He was already looking a little green, and had stubbed out the cigar.

Susan, seeing this, said quickly, 'Is that meal ready yet, Amanda? I'm starving!'

The meal was delicious and David soon lost his pallor. After dinner was over they returned to the armchairs, and everyone but David had brandy in delicately cut glass goblets, warmed to perfection.

Amanda began asking Dominic about his travels abroad and for a long while they listened while he recounted anecdotes about the people he had seen and the places he had visited.

He was a fascinating raconteur and Susan sat listening to him as though hypnotized by the sound of his deep, relaxed tones. She avoided looking at him as much as possible, but occasionally her eyes strayed in his direction and she discreetly studied the strong line of his jaw and the thick richness of his hair. His linen was immaculate and accentuated his dark colouring, and the lashes which veiled his eyes were long and thick.

But it was not his looks which attracted Susan. She had seen many handsome men who caused her not the slightest reaction. It was something more; a kind of animalism, which made her aware of the primitive emotions that run just below the surface of modern man. From Amanda's remarks she had gathered that, married or otherwise, Dominic Halstad was no saint, and the knowledge merely gave him an added attraction, a kind of dangerous temptation.

Realizing where her thoughts were leading her, she quickly brought them back to normalities. Why could not she remember she was an engaged woman, and act accordingly? She felt she was behaving, or feeling, like a schoolgirl with a crush on the headmaster.

It was eleven o'clock when David said, 'I think we ought to be going, Susan. It's getting late.'

Amanda stretched. 'It's only eleven, David.' She shrugged. 'But if you must, you must.'

Dominic rose to his feet. 'Can I give you a lift anywhere?' he asked.

'Thank you, but I have my car outside,' replied David. 'And thank you, Amanda. I've enjoyed myself enormously.'

Amanda stood up also. 'I'm so glad. We must do it again, eh, Susan?'

Susan nodded, and allowed David to wrap her cape about her.

'Yes, we must,' she said. 'Mr. Halstad's conversation was quite fascinating.'

'Yes, Dom ought to write a book,' said Amanda, looking playfully at Dominic. 'How about that, Dom?'

'Well, I will if I can borrow your secretary to do my typing for me,' he replied, watching Susan and seeing the hot colour surge into her cheeks.

David, too, saw his fiancée's embarrassment, and hastily drew her to the door.

'We must go. Good night, Mr. Halstad. Good night, Amanda.'

Outside the air was freezing, and Susan shivered. 'Central heating certainly makes you more vulnerable to the elements,' she said. 'Hurry up and let's get home, David.'

David put her into the car and then went to start it, but to Susan's dismay it would not start.

'Oh, lord,' muttered David. 'What a thing to happen on a night like this! It must be the cold air. It seems to have knocked all the life out of the battery.'

Susan saw the funny side and giggled. 'Well, shall I push, or will you?'

'Don't be ridiculous,' snapped David, unable to see anything amusing in their predicament.

'All right, all right. I was only trying to cheer you up.' Susan hunched her shoulders, and waited while David cranked the engine furiously.

'Shall I try and catch it on the accelerator?' she ventured, a few moments later.

'No.'

David was fuming, and Susan sighed. This would have to happen. Just when David was seeming a little more human, this occurred, and now he was sure to find it Amanda's fault in some way.

'If we hadn't spent so long in there, the damn car wouldn't have frozen like this,' he muttered, and Susan sighed again. Here it came! The same old story of recriminations. Anything but the real reason the car had defaulted.

Suddenly, the swing doors of the apartment building opened again, and a tall figure emerged, dressed in a thick fur-collared overcoat. It was Dominic Halstad, and Susan groaned inwardly. This would really settle things. David hated seeming at a disadvantage.

Dominic merely nodded to them and walked across to a dark-green Mercedes saloon that was parked just ahead of them.

David straightened up and looked at Susan. 'Shall I ask him if he will give you a lift?' he asked abruptly.

'No, of course not. I'll wait and go with you. We'll get away soon.'

David looked relieved. 'I'm sorry I bellowed at you,' he said awkwardly. 'I'm a bad-tempered cuss.'

'Don't be silly,' said Susan, smiling. 'Just hurry up and let's get going.'

Dominic Halstad had now opened the boot of his car

and was producing a coil of plastic-covered rope which he brought to David, saying casually:

'Would a tow be of any use?'

David lifted his head. 'Why . . . yes, it would. It's just the battery, I think. It's a bit flat.

'Okay. You fasten your end and I'll fasten mine. Give me a blast on your horn when you start up, right?'

'Right.'

David hastily tied the rope to his car, while Dominic connected the other end, and nodded briefly at Susan before sliding into the driving seat and starting up.

It only took a couple of hundred yards before David's engine fired and he tooted his horn to tell Dominic Halstad that he could continue under his own power.

The cars halted, the rope was put away and Dominic raised his hand in farewell, before re-entering his car and driving away.

'Good chap!' remarked David warmly. 'Not many men in his position would have been so helpful.'

'No,' agreed Susan. 'He didn't waste any time either.'

David nodded, and putting the car into gear they drove on to Susan's flat.

After arranging to spend the following day with David, Susan left him to enter the flat, which seemed very lonely tonight, knowing that Delia would not be returning.

She made herself a cup of cocoa, and carried it into the bedroom to drink while she undressed. But once in bed sleep was far from soon in coming. Her thoughts were too chaotic to allow her any peaceful rest, and restlessly she switched on the light again and reached for a half-finished novel she was reading.

As she read the words, however, they meant little to her. She found her mind drifting off at a tangent, and she found herself wondering again where Dominic Halstad's wife could be. He had not mentioned her and neither had Amanda.

Amanda had mentioned the life Dominic led as being unsuitable for a child and that could only mean one thing, surely! It was very puzzling.

Susan felt suddenly angry. It was not like her to indulge in idle speculation about anybody, least of all a man who could not possibly be of any importance in her life.

CHAPTER THREE

THE following week passed uneventfully until Friday. Delia had arrived back from Bristol full of excitement. Alan's parents had been dears, and had made her feel completely at home.

'I'm sure everything is going to turn out right for us,' she exclaimed on Monday morning while they were having their breakfast. 'Alan was marvellous to me and I really felt as though his parents liked me.'

'And why shouldn't they?' demanded Susan. 'You're a very likeable person.'

Delia sighed. 'Yes, but I mean, really liked me. You know . . . as a daughter-in-law. I'm sure Alan is going to ask me to marry him. Oh, Susan, wouldn't it be divine?'

Susan herself felt rather envious. If only David's mother had been like that, warm and welcoming. But she was glad for Delia's sake as Delia always seemed afraid that people would not like her.

When she arrived at the apartment on Friday morning, Amanda was not seated at her desk as usual. She always did her correspondence first thing in the morning, and Susan was surprised.

'I've arrived,' she called, before walking over to a radiator and warming her cold fingers.

She had not done much typing this week, apart from Amanda's letters, as Amanda had not yet begun a new novel and there was nothing else for her to do. They had spent most of the week driving in Amanda's car, sometimes with Susan at the wheel and sometimes with Sarah's husband, Bill, driving them. Bill had a regular job but acted as chauffeur for Amanda when she required him.

Amanda appeared just then from her bedroom and said, 'Hello, dear. I'm glad you're early. We've got a lot to do. Now, how would you like a trip to Paris?'

'Paris?' echoed Susan blankly.

'Yes, darling. Both of us, of course.'

'But when?' Susan was puzzled.

'Well, darling, we'll fly out this afternoon, spend the weekend in Paris and return home on Monday.'

Susan was still uncomprehending, and Amanda smiled. 'You know I had dinner with Dominic and Jon last night, don't you?'

'Yes.' Amanda had had dinner at Dominic Halstad's apartment here in town. Apparently he had a penthouse which he used whenever he was in London. Although he had intended bringing Jon for lunch one day, he had not found the time, and consequently he had invited Amanda to have dinner with them instead. Susan had been rather disappointed as she had been looking forward to meeting Jon, and to seeing Dominic Halstad again, although she did not like to admit the latter was true.

'Well,' continued Amanda, 'Jon is flying out to his aunt's today, to spend a week or so with her. Fay, Dom's sister, is married to a French count. They have a château near Fontainebleau, and although Jon is quite capable of conducting himself there, Dom has to be very careful that he's properly chaperoned.'

'Why?'

'Well, occasionally there've been threats of kidnapping

37

and so on, and a man as powerful as Dominic is bound to have enemies, don't you agree?'

'But he has no bodyguard.'

'No, I know. But that's not to say he shouldn't have. At any rate, Dom is rather a different kettle of fish. We're only concerned with Jon here. Well, what do you think?'

Susan sighed. 'I don't know what to think.'

'Why? Don't you find the prospect of a trip to France stimulating?'

'Of course, I do. It's just ... well ... it is the weekend, isn't it? And David is bound to expect me to spend my free time with him. I know he usually works on Saturdays, but there's all day Sunday —'

Amanda shrugged impatiently. 'It's only one day, Susan. Anyway, think it over for a few minutes while I go and help Sarah with my packing, and you can let me know your decision when I return.' She felt the coffee percolator on a nearby table and continued, 'The coffee is lovely and hot. Help yourself. I won't be long.'

Susan poured a cup of coffee, and sank weakly down on to a low chair. Here was her opportunity to get to know Dominic Halstad's son, at least. The prospect was exciting, and she felt her pulse leaping at the thoughts that invaded her head. It was all too tempting and Amanda was well aware of it.

Susan bit her lip hard. But what about David? Truthfully, he would only have one day to fill in, and anyway, last Sunday had been spent mainly in Medlar Grove and she could not face another day there in a hurry.

His mother had found fault with everything she had done, and as David spent most of the day working in the minute garden at the back of the old house, she had not seen much of him. Surely he would not mind if she went away, just this once, when he seemed to find plenty with which to fill time.

When Amanda returned, Susan said, 'I'd like to come. But what about reservations and things?'

Amanda smiled. 'They're already made. Dominic arranged it all last night.'

'You were sure I'd agree,' murmured Susan dryly.

'Well ... yes, darling. After all, if you don't see the world while you have the chance, once you're married to David you won't get a great deal of time. I can see that young man tying you down with an armful of children and then taking himself off to enjoy life. His type always do. He's very possessive, you know, and that way at least you aren't free to go wandering off if the fancy should take you.'

'Amanda, you're incorrigible!' exclaimed Susan helplessly, although she wondered if there was something in what Amanda said. David did tend to dwell often on the prospects of a family, and although Susan wanted children, too, she did not want to start a family straight away. 'Anyway,' she went on, 'why isn't his father travelling with him?'

'Oh, Dom isn't keen on acting as nursemaid.'

'To a fifteen-year-old? Good heavens, he doesn't need a nursemaid!'

'I know, but Dom has his work, too, you know.'

'Excuses, excuses,' said Susan, sighing. 'It seems to me your friend doesn't take his duties as a father seriously.'

Amanda shrugged. 'I wouldn't say that, Susan. Dominic and Jon are great friends. It's simply that Dom can't be bothered with the little things, the trivialities which some men enjoy. When you know him better you'll realize that for yourself.'

'I'm not likely to know him better,' remarked Susan, and sipped her coffee speculatively.

'Well, you'd better contact that young man and warn him that you won't be available until Monday evening,' said Amanda, changing the subject firmly.

'Dear me, I suppose I better had,' Susan grimaced. 'He doesn't like me to ring him at work.'

'Why, for heaven's sake? He's a partner in the firm, isn't he?'

'Yes, but he likes to keep his working life separate from his private life. He says I disturb his concentration when he's busy.'

Amanda raised her eyes heavenward and then turned away. 'Well, get it over with. There isn't a lot of time and you'll have to go home again and pack a suitcase. You'll need a change of clothes and an evening dress of some sort.'

'Why an evening dress? Are we going somewhere in particular?'

'We're flying out today, and spending tonight at Dom's apartment in Paris. Then, in the morning, we'll drive down to Fontainebleau with Jon. We're spending the night there and returning to Paris on Sunday. We might do a little sightseeing in Paris, stay Sunday night at the apartment again, and return home on Monday.'

'Oh! But I can't stay at this château. I mean, I don't know these people at all really, except through you. They won't be expecting me.'

'Yes, they will. Dom phoned Fay while I was there last evening. And he told her that you would probably be accompanying me, and then afterwards I spoke to Fay myself and she was most enthusiastic. You'll like Fay. She's only thirty-four. She was married when she was seventeen, and has three lovely children. Her husband, the Count, is a darling.'

Susan felt completely out of her depth. Going to Paris for a weekend was one thing; staying in a French château with a count and his family was quite another. She would not know what to talk about.

'Oh, really, Amanda, I think I'm going to back out of this,' she murmured self-consciously. 'I thought we were just taking this boy to Paris. I didn't imagine we were going to stay with Mr. Halstad's sister.'

'I know you didn't. But what does that matter? As I've said, you'll like Fay. She's not at all snobbish, if that's what you're afraid of. And the children are terrors. Quite ordinary and all that.'

'But a count . . .' said Susan helplessly. 'I wouldn't know how to address him.'

'Knowing Raoul, I should imagine he'll suggest you call him by his Christian name,' returned Amanda smoothly. 'Now come along, get that phone call made, and then get along home for your things.'

Susan felt she was being swept along on a strong tide that would not allow her to get away, and, unable to resist the temptation, she lifted the telephone. She thought, dryly, that Amanda had probably known about this trip earlier in the week, but had not said anything because she knew that, given time to think about it, Susan would certainly have refused, or allowed David to change her mind for her.

To her relief, David did not sound irritable when he answered the telephone and she said, tentatively: 'Darling, do you mind terribly if I go away with Amanda this weekend?'

David's good humour vanished, and he sounded annoyed. 'Away? Where to?'

'Paris. Amanda has to – deliver something to Paris, and has decided to go herself and spend the weekend there. She wants me to go – in case – in case she has any time for working.'

'That sounds rather fishy,' remarked David coldly. 'Now why are you really going?'

Susan sighed. 'Oh, really, David, don't you believe me? It's true. Amanda is taking some – one – to Paris.'

'Not some*thing*!'

'No. Jon Halstad.' Susan sounded a little weary.

41

'I thought as much. And is Dominic Halstad going too?'

'Of course not. Just Amanda and me and this boy. Oh, darling, you know last weekend you didn't have much time for me. Couldn't you agree for once that I'll have a much more exciting time there than spending the whole of Sunday with your mother?'

David snorted. 'My mother! I thought she would be brought into this. Just why did you ring me, Susan? Your mind is already made up, isn't it? You've decided to go and you're only letting me know, not *asking* me.'

Susan clenched her fists. David was right, of course. She had decided to go and she was merely going through the formalities by asking him for permission. She was being selfish, too, she supposed, but it sounded such a wonderful experience and spring in Paris was supposed to be quite something.

Aware that David was speaking again, she brought her thoughts back to the present.

'. . . and when may I expect to see you again? Monday?'

'Of course. We'll be back Monday morning. I'll be able to tell you all about it on Monday night.'

'Very well. But don't make a habit of it.'

Feeling like a prisoner who has been let out of jail on a weekend pass, Susan couldn't keep the excitement out of her voice, as she said:

'Thank you, darling. I'll be good.'

David grunted something in reply and rang off, and Susan replaced her receiver meticulously.

'That's settled, then,' said Amanda, and Susan became aware of her at her elbow.

'Yes, it's settled. But I do feel guilty, Amanda. I can't help it.'

Amanda shrugged. 'That will wear off,' she said bluntly. 'Now, you take a taxi back to the flat and collect your things. It's ten now; be back soon after eleven and we'll have an early lunch before leaving for the airport. Bill will take us. By the way, Jon is lunching here. He'll probably be here when you get back.'

'All right.' Susan rose to her feet. 'My tummy feels as though a rotor has been installed.'

Amanda grinned. 'Good. Bit of excitement is good for the juices. Don't be long.'

Susan packed her suitcase swiftly, then she climbed back into a taxi and drove to the store where Delia worked. She managed to contact Delia in the canteen and explained the position.

'How heavenly!' gasped Delia. 'A weekend in France. It sounds marvellous! Just the thing to tone you up. You've looked pretty fed-up at times this week. I was beginning to get quite worried about you.'

'Were you now? Well, there's no need. I'm fine.'

'You are now. You look as different again. You've lost that bored expression. What did David say?'

'Oh, the usual things. He wasn't very pleased, and I can understand that. After all, I don't suppose I'd like him to go flying off for a weekend on the continent without me.'

Delia linked her hands. 'Is this Dominic Halstad going to be there?'

'Good heavens, no! That's the reason we're going. If he were going there would be no need for Amanda to take the boy, would there?'

'No. I guess not. Well, have a good time.'

'Thanks. Actually, I'm a mass of nerves. How do you address a count?'

'Don't be silly, you'll be all right. If I know Amanda Blake she'll give you a marvellous time. Look at last year when you went to Portugal. You had a terrific time!'

Susan nodded slowly, and then glanced at her watch. 'Gosh, I must go. It's after eleven. See you Monday.'

43

'Okay,' Delia smiled, and Susan dashed off to find another taxi, feeling recklessly extravagant.

When she entered Amanda's apartment she immediately saw Jon Halstad. She would have recognized him anywhere. He was very like Dominic, with the same dark complexion, and lean good looks. His hair was curly, and he was dressed in a dark-grey suit with close-fitting trousers, and a white shirt. He looked about eighteen, and if she had expected some pale, wan, neglected teenager, dressed in jeans and a sweater, she was much mistaken. Jon Halstad was a strong, self-possessed young man, and he gave Susan a thorough appraisal as she removed her coat and advanced into the room.

His eyes took in the slim-fitting green suit with the fur collar, and the nylon-clad legs. Although he was not as tall as his father, he was still a little taller than Susan and in her high heels their eyes were on a level.

'Jon?' she ventured slowly.

'Yes. You must be Susan.' He smiled. 'My father told me you would be going with us. Tell me, do you know my father well?'

Susan flushed. 'Not very, why? Didn't he explain that I'm Amanda's secretary?'

'Oh, yes, he told me that. But I wondered . . .' His gaze slid away, and Susan felt mortified. Did he mean what she thought he was meaning? Surely not? Oh, God, she thought, what have I let myself in for?

She was relieved when Amanda came into the room, smiling cheerfully. 'Ah, there you are, Susan. Have you met Jon?'

'We've introduced ourselves,' said Susan, swallowing hard. 'Is there anything you want me to do?'

'No, I don't think so.' Amanda shook her head. 'Well, Jon, are you looking forward to going to your aunt's?'

Jon shook his head. 'Not particularly. Those kids are a bind.'

Amanda frowned. 'Jeremy is only a year younger than you,' she said. 'You ought to be good friends. And Yvonne is the same age as you, isn't she?'

'Oh, sure.' Jon shrugged. 'There's nothing to do there, though. Except go swimming in the lake.'

'And what thrills do you indulge in here in town?' asked Amanda dryly. 'You're not old enough to go night-clubbing yet, or has your father already initiated you into that art?'

Jon laughed, and Susan found herself laughing too. Amanda's expression was so comical.

'No, I don't go to night clubs. Just strip shows.'

Aware that he was teasing her now, Amanda chuckled. 'All right, Jon, I'm sorry. But please, try and enjoy yourself at Fontainebleau. Your aunt tries so hard to please you.'

'I know. Because I'm like Dad. She thinks the world of him, you know, and she hardly ever sees him.'

'Hmn. Dominic really does neglect his family, doesn't he?'

'All except one member,' replied Jon coldly.

Amanda walked across to the cocktail cabinet. 'I don't think we'll discuss your mother here,' she said firmly, and Jon shrugged.

'Just as you like. It's a great secret, isn't it? The skeleton in the Halstad family cupboard—'

'That will do, Jon,' said Amanda swinging round. 'I won't have you talking like that.'

To Susan's surprise, Jon immediately subsided. 'I'm sorry, A.B. It's just sometimes I get so sick of it all.'

'I know.' Amanda's voice was soothing. 'Now, what would you like to drink?'

During lunch, Susan hardly spoke a word. Instead she listened to Jon and Amanda. In a short while she learned a lot about Dominic Halstad, and she wondered why her brain captured every word they said about him, and

45

stored it up as though treasuring every scrap of knowledge. It was frightening. She felt as though she was walking along a precipice, with every chance of falling over the edge; but into what?

She learned that Dominic was away a lot and that Jon attended one of the better-known public schools. He was at present at the start of the Easter vacation. She learned that Dominic owned a house in the Lake District, and another in the south of France.

Jon seemed to be brought up mainly in the care of servants. His old nanny, Miss Carruthers, commonly known as Ruthie, divided her time between the London apartment and the Lakeland house and was there when he came home from school whenever his father was absent. Jon himself had travelled a lot, and had spent the last summer vacation with his father in the United States. Dominic had taken a house at Newport, Long Island, and they had had a marvellous time, swimming and water-skiing and sailing.

Susan mused that although Dominic did not devote a lot of his time to his son, such time as he did devote was well spent and they obviously got along very well together. They had a rapport which was not always evident with parents and children who were continually together and she found her earlier remarks not quite justified.

It was difficult to imagine life without the continual worry about money. To have an unlimited income certainly changed things considerably, and Jon talked of learning to fly a plane in the same way as most boys dream of learning to ride a motor-bike or drive a car.

He had everything money could buy. Horses; a small yacht on the lake near their home at Hawksmere; a movie-camera, with which he made colour films in his spare time; fishing equipment and skin-diving equipment (he told Susan that he and his father had spent Christmas

46

in the West Indies and he had learned to skin-dive while they were there), Susan lost count of the things he had seen and done. Yet when he spoke about them it was without any trace of boastfulness. On the contrary, he treated it all in a manner which Susan recognized as being very blasé, and she wondered what sort of a life he would have when at fifteen he had already done most of the things that a person waited a lifetime to achieve. Perhaps it was not so great after all to be affluent. How boring things would seem to Jon in a few years' time unless he changed drastically. No wonder the young men of his set tended to go off the rails a little. They were constantly craving some new thrill with which to banish their boredom.

After lunch they drove out to the airport. It was a bright, sunny afternoon with just a touch of frost in the air. Susan was wearing a scarlet anorak over her suit and looked young and appealing. Jon, in his short overcoat, looked almost as old as she did and Amanda remarked that they neither of them looked what they actually were.

Susan was seated beside Jon in the aircraft, as Amanda wanted to have a nap during the trip and, although she did not like the idea, as the journey progressed Susan found she was enjoying herself.

After his initial treatment of her she had expected a period of verbal sparring, but instead, Jon set himself out to be charming to her and she responded to his mood.

He told her about his life at public school, he described the house at Hawksmere, standing as it did at the head of the lake, a small jetty providing access to the water.

'The scenery is magnificent,' he said enthusiastically. 'I've been all over the world, but I love the Lake District. Not that a warmer climate isn't more pleasant, of course, but for sheer scenic enjoyment I like our home.'

'It sounds wonderful,' said Susan, sighing. 'I've never been to the Lake District.'

47

'Haven't you?' Jon sounded as though he was astounded. 'A.B. has been there. She wrote one of her earlier books at Hawksmere. Dad was away at the time and I was on holiday from prep. school. We had a grand time. She's a good sport, A.B.!'

'Don't you wish you could travel with your father all the time?' asked Susan. 'I mean, if your father spends a lot of time in the United States, couldn't you go to school there?'

Jon shrugged. 'Apparently not. At any rate, Dad prefers our schooling system. I attend the same school he used to attend, and I expect I'll go on to Cambridge as he did.'

'Oh,' Susan nodded. 'I suppose you miss him a lot?'

Jon shrugged again. 'Not in term time. During the holidays I usually see him, anyway, wherever he might be. I've spent holidays in practically every major country in the world.' He laughed. 'Except the really cold countries, of course.'

Susan was tempted to ask whether he spent any time with his mother and then restrained herself. She must not allow her curiosity to get the better of her.

They landed in Paris soon after four o'clock, and after the formalities went outside to where a low-slung continental limousine was waiting to take them to Dominic Halstad's apartment. Chauffeur-driven, the car looked luxurious and faintly exotic, standing there calmly waiting for them. Susan smiled to herself. How easy was life with someone always there to smooth the way for you.

Dominic's penthouse was situated in the Boulevard St. Hélène. A tall modern block of apartments, standing in exquisite gardens, they quite took Susan's breath away. She had never been this close to opulence before. In the forecourt, statuary and fountains took away the coldness of concrete and steel, and replaced them with sculptured lines surrounded by flowers and water. The futuristic design of the building was blended skilfully into its surrounding, and Susan could not wait to see inside.

Swing glass doors gave on to a cool marble-tiled entrance hall. Ahead of them stood six self-operable lifts and to the right were the porter's quarters: a self-contained flat. To the left a sign indicated 'Automobiles' and Amanda explained that the passage led to the under-ground garages.

It was all highly efficient and very convenient. The lift they entered transported them silently to the penthouse floor and they stepped out on to a pile-carpeted corridor. They walked along until they reached a door which had 'Halstad' written on it in little gold letters and Jon produced a key with which to open the door.

As they entered, a manservant glided forward to greet them, and Susan could only assume he had been fore-warned of their imminent arrival.

An elegant hallway gave into a low, light lounge, the walls of which were covered in hand-painted murals; exquisite murals, obviously done by a master hand. A pale-green Aubusson carpet flowed into every nook and corner of the room, while heavy green velvet curtains provided a frame for the wide windows. French doors opened on to a balcony, which overlooked the gardens, and which was large enough to accommodate a swing couch, an occasional table, glass topped for convenience, and several garden loungers. It was a veritable sun-trap and even so late in the afternoon was deliciously warm.

'It takes your breath away, doesn't it?' said Amanda shrewdly, watching Susan.

Susan smiled in a dazed manner. 'Yes. It's marvellous! Gosh, how the other half live!'

Amanda drew her brows together slightly. 'Don't be misled into thinking that Dominic came into all this,' she said. 'When he took over the chair on his father's death,

49

Halstad was no household name as it is today. He's built up the combine by his own efforts.'

Jon looked mockingly. 'And neglected everything else to do it,' he remarked dryly.

'That's not true, Jon, and you know it.' Amanda sounded angry. 'Your father is entitled to some credit. You've never wanted for anything in your life. If your father had been as indolent as your grandfather, you would have found your life immensely different. Dominic didn't get everything he wanted when he was a child. Money wasn't free-running for him as it is for you. Just remember that. And if you'd like to tell me that you would have preferred to have to work for what you needed, don't even attempt it. You're just not the type, Jon. If you're honest you'll admit that you have a lot to be thankful for.'

Jon smiled. 'All right, A.B., calm down! Good lord, what an advocate for Dad's cause you are, aren't you?'

Amanda chuckled. 'I suppose I am. But I don't like to hear you saying things against your father.'

'I'm not really. Oh, I grumble now and then, but I don't really mean it. I know Dad works very hard. I only wish he didn't go away so much.'

Jon stalked off to his bedroom and Susan looked surprised. 'When I asked him earlier if he missed his father, he said he didn't,' she exclaimed.

Amanda nodded. 'You have to get to know Jon before you can tell. He can talk a lot, and he seems pretty self-reliant, but he is only fifteen, you know, when all's said and done, and however he acts you have to remember that. Take what he says to you with a pinch of salt. He likes to think he knows all the answers, but he doesn't.'

Amanda seated herself on the swing couch on the balcony and said:

'Dominic prefers to stay at the apartment when he's in Paris. He's not too keen on hotels.'

Susan stretched wide her hands. 'After all this, I'm not surprised.' She lit a cigarette and walked over to the balcony rail, looking down on the tranquillity of the gardens, very different from the busy thoroughfare it joined. 'Do you think Mr. Halstad needs to spend so much time out of England? I mean, surely a man in his position could delegate much of the work.'

'True. I've wondered that myself. But Dom doesn't encourage anyone to talk about his occupation. And it's a long time since I've seen him, too. Perhaps he has other commitments.'

'Such as what?'

'That's what we would all like to know,' remarked Jon, as he emerged from the bedroom and came to join them, smiling sardonically.

CHAPTER FOUR

THE room Susan slept in had a white carpet. When her bare feet encountered its woolly pile the following morning, her toes curled appreciatively. She smiled to herself, remembering that when she was young she used to long for a room with a white carpet. In the orphanage she had occupied a bed in one of the dormitories, sharing the room with five other girls, and the image of a private bedroom all to herself had been just a dream.

And now, in this luxurious apartment, all her wildest dreams were being realized, for not only had her bedroom a white carpet, but the bathroom adjoining it was the utmost in elegant design, with real silver bathtaps and a circular bath surrounded by mirrors.

She chuckled to herself as she walked through to the

bathroom now and turned on the taps in readiness, comparing it to the tiled convenience she and Delia shared with the other tenants of Maxwell Close.

Glancing at her watch, she saw it was only seven-thirty, but used as she was to rising about this time she had not considered lazing in bed. Besides, it was all so new and exciting, she could not possibly contain herself a moment longer. The bed had been wonderfully comfortable; she had never slept between real silk sheets before. It was wonderful, too, to walk around in her dressing-gown without feeling the cold, such was the warmth of the heating system.

The previous evening, she and Amanda had spent a couple of hours after dinner walking through the Paris streets, and already she had seen the Eiffel Tower and the Arc de Triomphe. Jon had not accompanied them. He had seated himself in front of the television in the lounge and would not be moved. He scoffed at their enthusiastic appraisal of everything, and merely looked bored when Susan asked him whether he had been to the Louvre and Notre Dame.

'You forget,' Amanda had said to her, while they were drinking coffee outside a gay bistro in the Rue de la Madeleine. 'Jon has travelled since he was very small. He saw all these tourist attractions years ago, and although today he might appreciate them more, he's not sufficiently interested to make the effort to find out.'

Susan sighed now, and slipping out of her nightgown, she stepped into the porcelain depths of the bath.

She was drying herself when the door of her bedroom opened and she heard footsteps cross the room to the bathroom door and there was a tentative knock.

'*Mademoiselle?*'

'Yes.' Susan wrapped the towel closely round her. 'What is it?'

'I 'ave brought your breakfast, *mademoiselle*,' replied

52

the voice, and Susan recognized the maid who had served dinner the previous evening.

'Thank you,' she said quickly. 'Could you leave it on the table, please?'

'Of course. *Merci bien.*'

Susan heard the girl withdraw and close the bedroom door, and pulling on a white towelling bathrobe she had found hanging on the bathroom door she entered her bedroom again.

On a tray, a jug of coffee simmered merrily above a small burner, and beneath a warming plate she found hot rolls to have with a dish of yellow butter.

It all looked very inviting, and not waiting to dress, Susan sat down on the bed and began her breakfast. The coffee was strong and aromatic, and thoroughly continental in flavour. She found it quite delicious and drank several cups.

Afterwards, she walked over to the french doors which opened on to her own balcony and, opening them, stood breathing in the scented air. The bevy of flowers in the gardens below provided a perfume all their own, while the sights and sounds of Paris were a muted roar in the background that sent shivers of excitement up and down her spine. Not for anything would she have wished herself to be anywhere but where she was at that moment.

Realizing suddenly that she was wearing nothing but the bathrobe, she turned hastily and closing the french doors decided to get dressed. As she loosened the belt of the robe she wondered whom it belonged to, and for the first time became aware that it was much too big to belong to a woman. It could only belong to Dominic Halstad, and for a moment she felt a strange dizziness assail her. With reluctant fingers she threw the garment on the bed and turning swiftly she began to get dressed.

Her fingers were trembling a little, and she had to concentrate hard on what she was doing to prevent herself thinking thoughts which were wild and uncontrolled. She had got to stop thinking of the man in this way. It was pure madness, and forgetting her feelings of a moment ago she began wishing desperately that she had never come at all.

In addition to which she felt a certain amount of trepidation at the prospect of the coming thirty-six hours or so, which were to be spent at the Château des Etoiles. It was all very well for Amanda. She had known the Halstads since they were children. Susan was a very insignificant person when all was said and done, and was just not used to this kind of thing.

Dressed in a jersey shift of a greenish-grey colour, her hair caught up in a knot on top of her head, she emerged from her bedroom to find the lounge deserted. The maid was in the process of vacuuming the dining area and smiled encouragingly at her, as though aware of Susan's subdued attitude.

'Where is Miss Blake?' asked Susan, smiling in return. 'Is she up yet?'

'*Non, mademoiselle*. You are the first.'

'Thank you.' Susan walked across to the wide windows, which were closed now, and studied the magnificent view this room afforded of the whole of Paris. It really was amazing how far one could see, the slender ribbon of the Seine dividing the two halves of the city.

The maid finished her work and left the room, and Susan lit a cigarette and wandered over to the well-filled bookcase which ran along one wall. There was a varied miscellany of books, from classical novels to the latest spy dramas. Susan, who had always been taught that you could tell a person's character from the kind of books they read, found that it was utterly impossible to judge Dominic Halstad by his books. There was such a varied selection that it could not be done.

Lifting out a copy of *The Count of Monte Cristo*, one of

54

her own favourites, Susan seated herself on a low armchair and began to read. She was soon lost in the world of Edmond Dantès, and started when suddenly the telephone beside her began ringing.

Automatically, she picked up the receiver, not waiting for the maid to come and answer it, and not considering for a moment who it might be. After giving the apartment number, she said, 'Who is that, please?'

The operator answered and asked her to hold the line as they had a call for her from England. Immediately, Susan felt weak. There was surely only one person who could be ringing them from England, and she wished she had allowed the maid to come and take the call, for it would not be for her and she would then not have had to speak to him.

His deep attractive voice came as no shock as he said lazily:

'Is that you, A.B.?'

Susan swallowed hard. 'No, Mr. Halstad, it's me – Susan Stacey.'

'Oh, is it? Good morning, Susan. You're up bright and early.'

'Not really,' she replied dryly. 'It's eight-thirty, you know.'

'So it is.' He sounded amused. 'I wanted to speak to A.B. before she leaves for Fay's. Is she there?'

'She's not up yet, I'm afraid. Shall I ask her to take it on the extension, or can I take a message?'

'I think I can just about make do with you,' he returned mockingly, and Susan flushed angrily, wishing she could control her emotions more fully. It was awful that this man should be able to disturb her so. Aware that he was speaking again, she listened, trying to forget who was on the other end of the line, but all she could see were his lazy eyes and his attractive voice filled her head. 'Just give A.B. a message, will you? Tell her to ask

Fay to be in Paris next weekend. I want to see her. She'll understand.'

Susan bit her lip. 'Couldn't you have rung your sister and told her personally?' she asked, before she could prevent herself from voicing the question.

Dominic chuckled. 'I don't really know why I should explain my actions to you,' he remarked dryly, filling Susan with mortification at what she had done. 'But, since I'm sure your motives were purely innocent, I'll tell you. You will discover for yourself anyway this afternoon. The château is not connected to the telephone system. Does that satisfy you?'

Deciding she might just as well be hanged for a sheep as a lamb, Susan replied, 'But I understood that Amanda spoke to your sister on the telephone a couple of nights ago.'

'So she did. But Fay was at the Paris apartment at that time. She does have my permission to use it, you know. And a key, too, believe it or not.'

Susan felt as though her face would never resume its natural colour again. 'I see,' she murmured, and Dominic said easily:

'Relax. I don't mind you asking. If I had I shouldn't have answered your question. I'm quite capable of refusing to reply should I desire to do so.'

Susan swallowed again. 'Thank you, Mr. Halstad.'

'That's all right, *Miss* Stacey.'

He was laughing at her again, and she felt strangely upset.

'Is that all, then?' Her voice was very soft.

'I think so. Are you enjoying yourself?'

'Yes, thank you.'

'Oh, don't say that as though I were asking you if you were enjoying the Sunday school treat. What do you think of Paris? Are you looking forward to going to Fontainebleau?'

'I think Paris is wonderful, and as for going to your

56

sister's – well, I honestly have no idea how to treat them. After all, she is a countess, isn't she?'

'Yes. And Raoul is a count. So what?'

'It's easy for you to say that,' she replied, again astonished at her own daring.

'All right, Susan, I'm sorry if I'm teasing you a little. But don't worry. I'm sure both Fay and Raoul will adore you.'

Susan's stomach turned over. What did he mean?

'And now I must go. I have a lot of work to get through today,' he said smoothly. 'Good-bye for the present.'

'Good-bye, Mr. Halstad.' Susan reluctantly replaced her receiver. She had not wanted to stop talking to him. Not one tiny little bit!

She was idly staring into space, the novel open on her lap, when Amanda emerged from her bedroom in a long woollen dressing-gown. Brought abruptly back to earth by Amanda's entrance, Susan felt, and looked, rather guilty, and her employer eyed her wryly.

'Well, well. What illicit thoughts were you enjoying?' she asked, and Susan's face reddened anew.

'I don't know what you mean,' she exclaimed, and then shrugged. 'There's been a telephone call from Mr. Halstad.'

'Dominic? What did he want?'

'He asked if you would ask his sister to be in Paris next weekend, as he wants to see her. Don't ask me why. He didn't say.'

'I see. And what else did he say?'

'Nothing much. I'm afraid I always seem to do and say the wrong things where he's concerned.'

Amanda laughed. 'Don't tell me you were rude to him again.'

'Not exactly, but he does seem to rub me up the wrong way.'

57

Amanda compressed her lips. 'He certainly seems to have a strong effect on you, anyway. I'm not altogether sure that that's a good thing.' For once she was serious, and Susan bent her head and examined her finger-nails with assumed intensity.

'Why? Surely you don't imagine there's anything to be concerned about.'

Amanda shrugged and reached for a cigarette. 'Susan darling, I love you dearly, but you are rather – well, naïve in some ways.'

'Naïve?' Susan's head shot up. 'Me? Don't be ridiculous!'

'You are, dear, really. And vulnerable, too. You see, I adore Dom, and I'd never allow anyone to say a word against him, as a genuine person that is, but I'm not unaware of his propensity for women, and of the effect he has on them.'

Susan clenched her fists. 'But he's a married man. You told me yourself he had a wife.'

'I know. And so he has. But – well, theirs is not a normal marriage and Dominic is a normal man, with the usual male appetites.'

'I think that's disgusting.' Susan rose to her feet. 'I don't want to discuss this any more.' She pressed a hand to her throat and then turned and walked jerkily across to the window.

'You see what I mean.' Amanda sighed. 'You're very young and very naïve. And slightly narrow-minded, I think.'

'Narrow-minded? To think a man should be faithful to his wife?' Susan swung round. 'That's the last adjective I would have applied to myself. You should ask David. He thinks I'm too broad-minded, in lots of ways.'

Amanda snorted. 'I always said that young man was too big for his boots. Don't quote him to me, please.'

'Why not? He's my fiancé, after all. Why shouldn't I

say what I think? Oh, I wish I'd never come on this stupid trip at all!'

'So do I.'

Amanda ground her cigarette out in the ashtray, and aghast, Susan realized that she and Amanda were quarrelling for the first time in their association, and over a man who should have meant little or nothing to either of them.

'Oh, Amanda, I'm sorry.' Susan pressed the palms of her hands to her burning cheeks. 'I'm awfully sorry. I'm rude and a beast. Forgive me.'

Amanda herself was contrite, as she came over to Susan and put an arm about her shoulders. 'I'm sorry, too, Susan. I'm afraid I allowed my vivid imagination too much licence at that moment. But you've always seemed more like a daughter to me and I should hate you to do anything that you might later regret.'

Susan shook her head helplessly. 'Now what on earth am I likely to do? If you mean Dominic Halstad, I know I do find him attractive, physically, but I would never give up David for him. I love David. I presume this is what you're afraid of.'

'I suppose so. But, Susan, I'm very fond of Dominic and I should hate to find myself at loggerheads with him over you.' She held up her hand as Susan would have interrupted her. 'No, wait. I know Dominic, remember, and I was aware of how he was looking at you a few nights ago at the apartment. At the time I took no notice of it, but now, suddenly, he rings the apartment for no real reason, and speaks to you. To me it sounds—'

'He asked to speak to you, but I told him that you were still in bed.'

'If he'd really wanted to speak to me, he could have had the call put through on the extension, he knows that.'

'I know. I suggested it.'

'And what was his reply?'

59

Susan swallowed hard. 'He said it wasn't necessary.'

Amanda walked over to the french doors leading to the balcony. 'It's going to be a wonderful day.'

'Do I take it the subject is closed?' Susan watched her.

'For the moment.' Amanda opened the doors and stepped on to the balcony. 'I don't think I should ever tire of this view. It's magnificent.'

Susan sank down on to a low chair and lit herself a cigarette. She felt she needed one. Her head was whirling, and her stomach felt thoroughly disturbed. Amanda's words had frightened her a little, not only by their meaning, but by the strange and irresponsible way her own body had reacted. To be told a man like Dominic Halstad found you attractive was like drinking a bottle of some intoxicating spirit. It completely floored you, while all the time you were conscious that the effect was only temporary and sooner or later you would have to wake up.

How foolish she was to feel this way! Any man who was married and yet still allowed himself to have other women was utterly despicable, no matter how rich or influential he might be. Things might be different for the *dolce vita* set, but it was not like that for ordinary human beings, with jobs to do and homes to run. How lucky she was to have David, a solid young man with a steady job and no pretensions to things that were out of reach. She pitied Dominic Halstad's wife, whoever she might be. It must be terrible to be married to a man like that, not knowing where he was or who he was with. Was that why she was never heard of? Why she did not accompany him on any occasion?

Amanda came back into the room. 'Cheer up, darling. It's not the end of the world. Jon will be out shortly, and he will be sure to notice if you are downcast.'

'Jon. Oh, yes. Do you know, yesterday when I arrived

back at the apartment and found Jon, he asked me whether I knew his father very well. At the time I was astounded. Now I'm not at all surprised. It simply amazes me why I didn't realize sooner. Poor Mrs. Halstad!'

'Veronica!' Amanda shook her head. 'Yes, I feel sorry for Veronica, but not in quite the way you mean.'

'For goodness' sake, stop talking in riddles.' Susan stretched her arms. 'Let's drop it, as you said. I'll be on my guard against Dominic the Dreadful, and you can relax. Right?'

'All right.' Amanda smiled. 'I know you won't let me down.'

CHAPTER FIVE

Susan enjoyed the drive down to Fontainebleau. It was a beautiful morning and she soon found the shadows of the early morning dispersing in the blaze of noon. They arrived in the village of Chabriond at eleven-fifty and drove between the whitewashed cottages and up a steep incline towards the end of the valley.

Long before they reached the Château des Etoiles, its tall imposing turrets could be seen above the surround of trees, making it appear as some fairy-tale palace with the sun glinting on the slim windows, and adding a sheen of gold to the grey stone masonry.

Susan sat forward in her seat, enthralled by her first sight of the château. It stood at the head of the valley with an uninterrupted view of the countryside spread out around it. As they drew nearer, and the trees thinned, Susan could see a small ornamental lake in the foreground in which swam several graceful swans, adding to the illusion of a stage backcloth.

The car turned between iron gates, adorned with the crest of the St. Lucien family, of which Raoul St. Lucien was now the head.

'*Le Château des Etoiles*,' remarked Susan softly. 'What a lovely name. The Castle of Stars.'

Amanda smiled. 'Yes, it is rather nice, isn't it?'

'I think it's overdone,' remarked Jon dryly. 'Why ever Aunt Fay had to marry a Frenchman, I'll never know.'

Susan raised her eyebrows at him. 'And why not?'

Jon shrugged. 'I don't hold with all this hand-kissing and bowing.'

Amanda laughed. 'Perhaps when you get a little older, you'll find that hand-kissing and bowing get you a little farther than "Hi, folks!"' she replied smoothly. 'I'm convinced a woman must feel more feminine when she's treated with grace and charm, in place of casuality –'

Susan giggled helplessly now. 'Oh, honestly, Amanda, I don't think there is such a word as "casuality". It sounds too much like casualty.'

'Which is what you will be, if you talk to me like that,' returned Amanda, chuckling herself.

The chauffeur brought the car to a halt before the shallow flight of steps which led up to the solid oak front door, embellished by heavy black hinges and a lion's head knocker.

'Well, my dears, we've arrived!'

Amanda stepped out of the car without waiting for the chauffeur to assist her and looked up at the imposing façade of the small castle. It really was remarkably well preserved, and Susan, stepping out beside her, found her earlier nervousness vanishing in the new-found delight of discovery.

'It's marvellous,' she exclaimed. 'Amanda, I am glad I came! I wouldn't have missed this for the world!'

The massive door was opened just then and two young people came jumping down the steps to greet them. Although Susan had been told that they were practically the same age as Jon she could see why he felt superior to them. Jeremy at fourteen was a typical schoolboy in shorts and a tee-shirt, his hair cut long with a fringe. Yvonne, a year older at fifteen, was smaller than her brother and had her hair in plaits and wore shorts and a tee-shirt like her brother. Compared to them, Jon seemed much older and quite sophisticated.

'Auntie Amanda! How wonderful to see you!'

The two children's attention was held wholly by Amanda, and Susan glanced at Jon, wondering how he felt to be ignored like this. For a moment she surprised a look, a little like envy, on Jon's face, and then it was gone, and he assumed a bored expression. At that moment, Susan realized what was wrong with Jon. He had been treated as an adult too soon. He had missed those years between boyhood and manhood and had been expected to switch from being a boy to maturity without any of the special years in between. Without the understanding of a mother, such things were difficult to achieve and Susan found her thoughts turning yet again to the mystery of Veronica Halstad. Why couldn't she bring up her own son? Apparently this 'Ruthie' person was too old to realize just what Jon was missing. And Jon himself felt out of place here. These children would not be able to communicate with him and through no fault of his own he was becoming an introvert, or so it seemed to Susan. No boy of fifteen should be expected to dress and act like an eighteen-year-old all the time. It just was not healthy. He needed to be changed out of those clothes he was wearing so casually, into jeans and tee-shirts, and be allowed to act his own age and grow up in his own time.

It was strange how involved she was becoming with

the Halstad family, Susan thought rather wearily, but in Jon's case it was impossible to ignore such an unconscious appeal for help. Something had got to be done. But how?

Amanda introduced Susan to Jeremy and Yvonne and she found them quite charming. They spoke perfect English, which was not surprising as they both attended English public schools. Jeremy could have attended the same school as Jon, but the Count himself had been educated in England and consequently Jeremy went to his father's old school, just as Jon went to Dominic's.

Amanda explained all this during the course of introductions and Jeremy half-heartedly greeted his cousin and asked him about their journey.

They all mounted the steps to the ornate entrance of the château. A stiffly attired major-domo in dark-green livery had appeared, and seemed to be instructing the chauffeur about the luggage, and feeling slightly bemused Susan made her entry into the château.

They entered into a massive hall, oak panelled and with a polished timber floor strewn carelessly with thick Bokhara rugs. Although it was a warm day, a huge fire burned in the grate, which alone seemed big enough to roast an ox, and Yvonne explained that a central heating system was run as well from a furnace in the basement. 'Stone buildings require concentrated heating to keep them at living temperature,' she said, grimacing.

'Mother is instructing Cook about lunch at the moment. There's been rather a panic this morning because Cook and the new housekeeper don't see eye to eye on anything and because she has this dinner party this evening, Mother has been trying to keep the peace.' She smiled. 'So she asked me to make her apologies and she'll greet you as soon as she can.' She looked at Susan. 'Would you like some coffee or would you both rather be shown to your rooms?'

Jon had disappeared with Jeremy, and Amanda said

briskly, 'Well, I'd prefer to freshen up, I think. How about you, Susan?'

'I think that would be the best idea,' agreed Susan, smiling. 'I'm absolutely dying to see more of this place. It's terrific!'

The staircase was wide but steep, and at the top passages led off in all directions. Here the floors were thickly carpeted and the walls were hung with hand-made tapestries. Susan felt as though she had been transported back in time and said so.

'It is nice, isn't it?' Yvonne was obviously proud of her unusual home. 'Daddy inherited it from Grandfather about ten years ago. Before that we spent some time in Paris, but this is loads better. We couldn't have animals at the apartment and it was ghastly. Here, both Jeremy and I have two dogs each, and then, of course, there are the horses. We have quite a stable.' She looked at Susan. 'Do you ride?'

Susan shook her head. 'I'm afraid not.'

'You must learn. Perhaps Daddy would teach you. He's a wonderful rider, isn't he, Auntie Amanda?'

'Wonderful,' agreed Amanda, smiling. 'But I'm afraid Susan and I are only here until tomorrow, so she'll hardly have time to learn, will she?'

'Oh, that's a pity. Why don't you stay longer? I'm sure Mummy would adore to have you. She loves company. We're so isolated here, really.'

Amanda patted Yvonne's shoulder gently. 'I don't think you ought to issue invitations in such a fashion, young lady,' she remarked dryly. 'Particularly as you've just told us your mother is having difficulties with the staff.'

Yvonne giggled. 'Perhaps not, but never mind.'

'Anyway, who's making up the dinner party this evening?' asked Amanda suddenly. 'I hope your mother hasn't gone to a lot of unnecessary trouble just for us.'

'Oh, don't be silly. You know Mummy adores arranging dinner parties. Anyway, it's only a small affair. Apart from Miss Stacey and yourself, and the family of course, there are only to be about thirteen others.'

'Making twenty in all,' said Amanda, sighing. 'Really, Yvonne, your mother is the very limit.'

Susan clasped her fingers tightly round the strap of her handbag. A dinner party of twenty was a *small* affair. Just what was considered a large affair? And how on earth would she manage to converse if they were French?

The rooms Susan and Amanda were to occupy were only separated by a bathroom, which they were to share. The rooms, both alike, were high and narrow with slender windows overlooking the sweep of the valley, with the river curving lazily down its centre. Although they were on the first floor they seemed terribly high and Susan wondered whether it was possible to walk in the battlemented surround that curved round the turrets.

After a swift wash, and a renewal of her make-up, Susan descended the stairs again to be met at the bottom by Jon on his way up.

'Well, princess,' he said mockingly, 'have you explored your ivory tower?'

'Don't be sardonic. It doesn't suit you,' retorted Susan easily. 'I think this is a wonderful place, and you'll not make me change my mind.'

'Bravo! Bravo!'

Susan felt the ready colour rush to her cheeks as a tall man crossed the hall towards them.

Jon gave Susan an amused glance and then said, 'Uncle, allow me to present Miss Susan Stacey, A.B.'s secretary. Susan, this is the Comte de St. Lucien.'

He ended his words with a flourish and Susan felt embarrassed and restrained.

'I trust you will ignore the deplorable manners of my

66

young nephew, *mademoiselle*,' said Raoul St. Lucien charmingly. 'I can assure you he is at pains to appear sophisticated, a man of the world. Me, I prefer children to be children, until it is time for them to grow up.'

'Oh, I agree,' said Susan fervently, and allowed the Comte to take her hand and raise it almost to his lips. Jon looked on stoically, and then turned and ran swiftly up the flight of stairs.

'So! You like my castle, Miss Stacey?' The Comte released her hand and cupping her elbow led her across the wide hall and into a charming lounge the windows of which had been widened and enlarged to encompass a delightful view of the lake and the swans, the larches and pines forming a dark background.

'Please call me Susan. And yes, I think it's a wonderful place, and yet it's really a home.'

'Thank you . . . Susan. And you must call me Raoul. Please—' as Susan would have protested. 'I insist. These days a title in France means little, and it is well that it should be so. After all, I am but a farmer. I have a vineyard, and I grow root crops. What else could I be? My family have been farmers for generations.'

'But you used to live in Paris.' Susan could have bitten out her tongue. One of these days it would get her into serious trouble. What business was it of hers what the Count did in Paris?

'Yes. I attended an agricultural college for a time, and then later I divided my time equally between here and Paris. But Etoiles was always my home.'

'I see. I ask too many questions. I'm sorry.'

'Nonsense. How else are we to learn, except by asking questions? I encourage my children to be inquisitive. It is a good fault.'

'But I am hardly a child,' Susan smiled.

'Indeed you are not. And I am neglecting my duties as a host. What would you like to drink?'

When Amanda joined them, they were drinking Martinis and discussing the merits of different wines as though they were old friends. Indeed, Susan felt that she had made a friend. The Count was so relaxed and so easy to talk to that she had quite forgotten he was indeed a count. With him there was no awareness of the sexes; they were simply two people who found things of mutual interest to talk about.

Fay St. Lucien was the complete antithesis of all Susan's imaginings. Knowing Dominic Halstad and his dominant character, she found Fay vastly different. She was small, and slender, and was fair, much to Susan's amazement. She was friendly and unassuming, and had a merry tinkling laugh. She obviously adored her handsome husband, and he felt the same about her. Their complete unity in everything made Susan doubly conscious of Jon, and of how different he must feel to them. Jeremy and Yvonne were warm and secure in the knowledge of their parents' love for them and for each other and Jon must feel very much the interloper. It made her angry, too, that Jon should have had to sacrifice so much for his father's selfishness, for what else could it be?

Lunch was served in the small but comfortable dining-room adjoining the lounge, and afterwards Amanda declared that she was going to rest on her bed.

Jeremy and Yvonne invited Jon to go riding with them and after the Count had departed about his estate duties, Susan found herself alone with Fay.

'Come along,' said Fay, smiling, 'let's go back into the lounge. We can take the coffee-pot and have a cigarette in peace.'

It was very pleasant, sitting smoking and drinking coffee and Susan relaxed.

'Did Amanda give you the message from your brother?' she asked suddenly.

'From Dom? No. What message?'

Susan relayed the message and Fay nodded, her expression suddenly very solemn.

'Thank you, Susan,' she said. 'I wonder what's going on now.'

Susan remained silent, determined to guard her impulsive tongue.

'Tell me,' said Fay suddenly, 'do you know about Veronica?'

Susan went scarlet. 'No. I'm afraid I know very little about your brother or his wife. I've only met him once.'

'And what did you think of him?'

Susan shrugged. 'I don't know. He seems a very dominant personality.'

'Yes, he is. Which is just as well in the circumstances. Poor Dom. He's had a hell of a life!'

Susan stubbed out her cigarette. She did not know what to say. She wanted to stop Fay from talking about her brother to her. She was thinking about him far too much already and Fay's confidences should not be for her ears.

'You have an amazing view of the valley from the bedroom windows,' remarked Susan, for something to say. 'I must say I've never had such an exciting experience as this trip.'

Fay looked at her shrewdly. 'Are you not, then, interested in my brother?' she asked bluntly.

Susan sighed, and looked down at her toes. Then she looked up at Fay, honestly. 'Yes,' she said simply, 'I'm interested in your brother, but I don't think you ought to discuss his affairs with me.'

'Why? Has Jon been warning you of the terrible skeleton in the Halstad family cupboard?'

'How did you know?'

Fay laughed, albeit a little sadly. 'Jon likes to exaggerate everything, and I imagine Amanda has been embroidering the tale as usual. I'm afraid at times her imagination runs away with her. I can quite believe you've got to the point where you're almost frightened to hear what it is.'

Susan found herself smiling at Fay's words. Like her brother she had the knack of hitting the nail on the head immediately.

'I can see from your expression that I'm right.' Fay smiled rather ruefully. 'It's quite simple really. My sister-in-law is an alcoholic.'

Susan stared at Fay. Her body felt suddenly very cold. This was something she had never even imagined. For a moment, she had thought that Veronica might be insane, but that she might be depraved in any way had never occurred to her. It did not condone Dominic's attitude to living, but at least it explained his cavalier treatment of women.

'So now you know.' Fay lay back in her seat and blew cigarette smoke into the air in rings. 'She's in a home for alcoholics at the moment, recovering from her latest binge.' Her voice was scornful. 'She became bored, you see, when she found that all Dominic really wanted was a home and a family. She'd expected a life of a different kind. She wanted to move with the playboy crowd, going from place to place with them, and doing what they do, which is precious little apart from debauchery. That would have suited her, though. She always liked plenty of men around.' Fay sounded disgusted. 'It's ironic that now she's degenerated as she has she has driven Dominic into the kind of life she always wanted. They split up after Dominic became chairman of the company.'

'And will she be cured?'

'If she seriously tried she might be, but that's not very likely. She only submits to treatment because Dominic insists and, after all, he supports her financially. And her succession of hangers-on.'

'I see. That's why I've never read anything about her.'

'Yes. It's a well-kept secret, and Dominic never admits anything.'

Susan shook her head. 'It's unbelievable! Why should anyone with their kind of money and background become bored enough to become like that?'

'Money can only make you happy so long as the novelty of having it is there. Once the novelty wears off, well . . .' Fay shrugged.

'I see.' Susan drew hard on her cigarette. 'I think I forejudged your brother.'

'Did you? Perhaps he does deserve a little of your censure. He's rather a cynical man these days, as you can imagine. Especially where women are concerned. Veronica saw to that.'

'Does Veronica live in London, then?'

'No. Mostly in the States. The clinic she is at present inhabiting is in New York.'

'Oh! Is that why Mr. Halstad spends so much time in the United States?'

Fay made a moue with her lips. 'I doubt that he spends any longer in the States, than in, say, Hongkong, for example.'

'Does Jon know about his mother?'

'Oh, yes, he knows. But he never sees her. She has no interest in him, and honestly I don't think Dom is keen. You can understand that.'

Susan shook her head. 'It's very sad.'

Fay shrugged. 'Sad? I suppose for Dom and Jon. For Veronica, well . . . who knows? She seems uncaring of whom she hurts in the process.'

When the children returned, afternoon tea was served and then Fay excused herself, and went to see about the final arrangements for the dinner party. Susan, left to herself, decided to explore the grounds, and going out through the French doors leading from the lounge on to the terrace, she descended the steps and walked towards the ornamental lake.

It was very peaceful, and she walked along the pathway leading round the lake, enjoying the sounds of the birds settling down in the dusk and the rustling in the undergrowth as the small, wild creatures that come out at night made ready for their evening's activities.

Already the air was much cooler, here above the valley, and the tops of the trees were beginning to move in a gentle breeze. Susan wondered what it would be like in the castle when a full-force gale was blowing outside. It must be wonderful to feel safe and secure inside its grey walls with a storm tearing the sky to ribbons, and bending the tall pines from their lofty peaks.

She returned to the castle to find Jon already dressed for dinner, lounging in an armchair with an evening paper. As the paper was in French, Susan said:

'My, my, you are clever!'

Jon looked up with a grin, and Susan found herself responding instinctively. He really was very like his father, and she felt her stomach turn over inexplicably. She realized, too, that for most of the day thoughts of David and her life at home seemed completely out of touch. She had become so absorbed in other things.

She passed through the lounge and mounted the stairs to her room. She could hear Amanda in the bathroom, so she removed her clothes, slipped on a dressing-gown and went to the wardrobe to take out the dress she was to wear that evening. Her suitcase had been unpacked in her absence and the dress, when she removed it from its hanger, had obviously been pressed in readiness for the dinner party. Unused to such treatment, she smiled wryly. It would be fatally easy to become addicted to this kind of life, she thought. Addicted! Addicted! Now why on earth had that word come to mind? That was something she did not want to think about and she was determined to remove all trace of Dominic Halstad from her thoughts.

The dress she had brought to wear that evening was a long hostess gown of oyster-coloured slip jersey, with a high upswept collar which emphasized the slim line of her throat, and long sleeves which were gathered into pleats at the wrists. The skirt was smooth and hung in folds to Susan's ankles. At the time she had bought it in a fit of extravagance, she had wondered whether she would ever have the opportunity to wear it, and tonight gave her the perfect excuse. David, who had been shown the gown at the time she brought it home, had thought it rather uninspiring, and much too plain, but tonight, with her thick hair curving loosely about her shoulders it would look utterly delightful.

Amanda came to her room, just as she was running a final comb through her hair, and entered with her usual lack of formality.

She halted, taken aback by Susan's appearance, and said, 'That dress, Susan! Wherever did you get it?'

Susan looked startled. 'Why? Is something wrong?'

'Not in the least. It suits you perfectly. I simply was astounded at your appearance. You look fabulous, my dear.'

Susan chuckled. 'Well, thank you. You don't look so bad yourself.'

Amanda was wearing a heavy silk dress in a dark-green colour in deference to the occasion, and Susan wondered whether Fay realized just what an achievement this was, getting Amanda out of tweeds!

They went down together to find a group of people now in the lounge, which had miraculously been enlarged. A pair of sliding doors had been removed to reveal

73

another room, very much like the lounge, and the over-flow from the lounge now converged here. A bar had materialized in a corner and a white-clad barman was dispensing drinks to a bevy of waitresses. Susan was quite alarmed at the sight of so many strange faces, and Amanda had to urge her forward to where Fay and Raoul were standing talking to some of their guests.

Introductions were made and Susan found herself grappling with a strange assortment of foreign names, some of which seemed quite incomprehensible.

Jon appeared at her side, and whispered, 'What's the matter, honey? Do you need a friendly hand to hold?'

Susan smiled. 'I must admit, I do find all this a little intimidating.'

'But why? You look charming. And most of these women are absolutely dying to know who you really are and what you do. But don't enlighten them. Let them go on guessing. They'll have you as a fugitive debutante in no time at all.'

Susan burst out laughing, and then blushed as her laughter attracted the attention of almost everyone in the room. She was relieved when they went in for dinner and she could absorb herself in her food to the exclusion of everything else. To her relief she found she had Jon on one side of her, although the gentleman on her other side spoke perfect English and managed to draw her out of herself a little by inquiring about Amanda's books.

The dinner seemed to last for ages, and Susan found herself wishing it was over. Although it was exciting meeting all these people, many of whom had titles of their own, she found even this could become a little monotonous in time and she began to realize that bore-dom could be found even here.

Perhaps if their conversation had been other than pre-dominantly French she would have enjoyed it more. As it was, although she spoke a little French, their swift way of speaking made it impossible for her to follow them and she merely had to listen and pick up a word here and there.

Amanda, an eloquent linguist, found no difficulty at all, and even Jon seemed quite at ease.

She accepted a cigarette from the man on her right hand, and after it was lit she lay back in her seat, and began wondering what would happen when they rose from the table. Would there be dancing? Or would they play cards? Perhaps both!

Coffee was served in the lounge with liqueurs and the men smoked Havana cigars which smelled delicious.

Jon appeared at her side and said, 'You look quite blasé. Has our illustrious atmosphere begun to pall already?'

Susan shook her head vigorously. 'Of course not. It's just that I'm a little out of place here, that's all.'

'Don't be silly. Of course you're not. Anyway, there's to be dancing later in the hall for the younger ones. I expect the others will play cards.'

'What do they play? Bridge?'

'Are you kidding?' Jon laughed. 'No, not bridge. Maybe a little chemmy ... or vingt-et-un or whatever they're playing in fashionable circles at the moment.'

'Oh!' Susan nodded. 'I must say I do feel a little naïve, now.'

Jon grinned. 'You're just a nice girl who's been catapulted into a society that seems completely alien. You'll get used to it.'

'I doubt that very much.'

Jon went off again, and Susan sipped her coffee pensively. She wondered whether it would be possible for her to slip away somehow and avoid the rest of the entertainment. She felt rather lonely and out of place, whatever consolation Jon might afford, and she would quite willingly spend the rest of the evening lying on her bed with a good book. She had brought a paperback that she was reading with her, and it was quite absorbing. Sufficiently so, at any rate, to warrant a couple of hours spent on it.

She rose to her feet and was crossing the hall when she heard the sound of a car door being slammed and footsteps mounted to the front door. It was opened with deliberation and the man who entered caused Susan to halt in her tracks, while her legs turned to water beneath her. Dressed tonight in a black astrakhan coat of thigh length, open to reveal a dinner jacket and the brilliant whiteness of his shirt front, Susan could only stare at him, feeling rooted to the spot.

He closed the door quietly, and walking lazily across to her said, 'What's the matter? Are you all right?'

Susan's heated cheeks infuriated her and she said uneasily, 'Of course, I'm fine. I was just startled to see you, Mr. Halstad. After all, you are the last person I would expect to see here, aren't you?'

Dominic Halstad stood, legs apart, his hands thrust into the pockets of his coat, and Susan thought he epitomized power and influence and magnetism. She felt helplessly aware that her feelings towards him were becoming somehow absolute, and it was petrifying. David, she said to herself furiously, David! You must think of David!

'And how are you enjoying yourself?'

Susan swallowed hard. 'Why, I –'

'Or were you tiptoeing away to your room just now? You look guilty.'

But not for those reasons, thought Susan, with an hysterical desire to laugh.

'Well, actually, I feel rather out of place,' she confessed quietly. 'I'm not at home here. I don't belong. Amanda is different. She's used to this kind of society even if she doesn't mix in it very often.'

'That's nonsense,' said Dominic Halstad, overriding her attempted denial. 'Perhaps it's because they're all foreigners. Don't you speak French?'

'A little. Not a lot, though.'

'That must be it, then. But never mind. I'm here now. You can talk to me.'

'I can't think what we might have to talk about,' retorted Susan, with an attempt at dignity.

'Can't you now? Well, that's interesting. We'll have to find a mutual interest. How about writing? You must be interested in that, seeing that you work for an authoress. I'm interested in writing myself. I used to be a reporter at one time. A long, long time ago, of course. Probably before you were even born.'

Just then Raoul appeared in the doorway of the lounge. He must have been informed of his brother-in-law's arrival, for he came walking across to them, holding out his hand, a welcoming smile on his face.

'Dominic! How good it is to see you again. And what a surprise. We understood from Amanda and Jon that there was no question of you coming at this time.'

Dominic looked a little sardonic. 'Yes, but I changed my mind. I decided the break would do me good. How are you, Raoul?'

Feeling an unwanted third again, Susan began to drift towards the stairs, until Dominic Halstad's voice stopped her. She had thought he had simply been trying to cheer her up before Raoul's appearance, and she felt embarrassed when he said:

'Come back here, Susan. You can talk to me while I have something to eat. I suppose I do warrant a meal, do I, Raoul?'

Raoul nodded and said, 'Of course,' but Susan was aware that he was looking at her a little strangely. Good lord, she thought anxiously, surely he doesn't imagine that Dominic and I —! Surely not! She found she was thinking of him as 'Dominic' and the knowledge frightened her. She was getting out of her depth, and sliding deeper every moment.

'I'd rather go to my room, thank you,' she said firmly, but Dominic's eyes were taunting her now. She had the feeling that he knew the turmoil she was suffering and was deliberately provoking her.

'Don't be silly. It's only nine-thirty. Come on, I'll show you the part of the château the guests never see.'

Susan had no choice but to follow him. If she had refused it would have looked as though she was being rude, and however she felt she could not offend him, if only for Amanda's sake. Oh, Amanda, she silently begged, appear now, and rescue me before it's too late.

Raoul had to go back to his guests and Dominic said he was quite capable of dealing with the cook himself. Susan did not doubt it. His manner left no room for complacency.

The cook greeted him like a long-lost relative and chattered volubly to him in French, answered just as casually by Dominic. He was seated at the scrubbed wooden kitchen table and a meal fit for a king was produced in a very short time. Cold meats and salads, consommé and oysters, fresh fruits and wines.

The cook left them in peace after she had seen that Dominic had everything he wanted and he said, 'Sit down!' to Susan as she stood awkwardly leaning against the dresser that was set with shining plates and swinging cups on their hooks.

Sighing, she did as she was bidden, and said at once, 'Look, Mr. Halstad, your brother-in-law has got entirely the wrong impression from this and I wish you would disillusion him as soon as possible. I'm here as Amanda's companion, not yours.'

Dominic looked up at her, grinning, and then fastened

his white teeth on to the tender flesh of a chicken leg. Chewing, he eyed her speculatively, and she wished herself far away. His studied appraisal was nothing short of insolent and she said hotly:

'For goodness' sake, stop it!'

'Why? Don't you like men to look at you?'

'That's not the point. You aren't just *looking* at me. And I don't like it.'

'All right.' His eyes were mocking, as he raised a cut-glass goblet of wine to his lips.

Susan moved uncomfortably. His every action seemed calculated to disturb her and he was succeeding admirably. Was he really aware of what he was doing, or was he simply befriending a fellow countrywoman in another country? The latter seemed highly unlikely. Dominic Halstad was not the type of man to be unaware of his physical appeal.

'Tell me,' he said suddenly, as he pared a golden peach, 'what do you think of Jon?'

Glad of the respite, Susan shrugged. 'I like him,' she said simply. 'But he's a very lonely child.'

'Lonely? Is he? I wouldn't have thought so.'

Susan stared at him, staying the ready retort that came to her tongue.

'In what way is he lonely?'

'Well, he's too old for his age. He doesn't know how to act like a child any more. He's neither an adult nor a child. And I think he's missing his youth. You're expecting too much from him.'

'Indeed!' Dominic studied her again. 'And does your wide experience of life entitle you to express opinions of this kind?' he asked sarcastically. 'I mean, being a woman of the world, and all that jazz —'

Susan rose to her feet. 'You just love tormenting me, don't you?' she exclaimed bitterly. 'Well, you aren't going to do it any longer. And if you weren't so engrossed

79

with your own appetites you might spare a thought for your son's—'

For a moment there was complete silence in the room and all that could be heard was the ticking of the clock on the dresser and the faint sounds of music from the hall.

Susan was horrified. What had she done? How had she dared to speak to him like that? What must he think of her?

She pressed a hand to her stomach and stood looking at him, waiting for the bomb to fall.

In silence she watched him rise to his feet and walk round the table towards her, stopping in front of her so that he was so close their bodies were almost touching.

'So that's what you think,' he murmured, his eyes brilliant and hypnotic in the dull lights. The electricity at the château was run from their own generator and tonight, with the hall needing so much light, the kitchens were inclined to be rather gloomy.

'I – I – I suppose I should say I'm sorry,' she began. 'It's nothing to do with me, after all.'

Dominic's breath fanned her cheek and she wanted to move away, far away, as far as possible. This was danger, with a capital D, and she dared not consider the consequences.

'Do you have any idea what would have happened if anyone else had said that to me?' he muttered, his voice husky now.

Susan looked up at him. She had been avoiding doing so, but now she could not stop herself, and he said, with a groan, 'Oh, *God*!'

Suddenly the kitchen door was opened, and abruptly Dominic turned away from her, to confront Amanda.

Amanda's shrewd gaze took in the picture of guilt that Susan appeared to be, and she said, rather shortly:

'So here you are, Susan. I've been looking for you.'

'She's quite safe,' remarked Dominic dryly, reseating himself at the table without waiting for Amanda to leave. He seemed unusually terse and Amanda felt perturbed. What had been going on here? Just what had she interrupted?

'So I see,' she said. 'Well, Susan, are you coming?'

Susan roused herself from the feeling of inertia which had possessed her a few moments ago.

'Of course, Amanda. I'm sorry, but Mr. Halstad asked me to talk to him while he was having a meal.'

'Indeed. Raoul told me you were here, Dominic. To what do we owe the honour of this appearance? I understand Fay has been trying to persuade you to come here for months. Without any success, I might add.'

Dominic lay back in his seat and swung it round on its back legs to face Amanda.

'I must say your welcome overwhelms me,' he remarked coolly. 'Don't get so het-up, A.B. Your little ewe lamb will come to no harm at my hands, I can assure you. It seems blatantly obvious that she is your protégée, as well as your secretary.'

Amanda sighed. 'Dominic, please! I can only assume that you've been drinking, for I don't know what you're talking about.'

'Don't you? Well, perhaps it's just as well.' His eyes turned to Susan, and as she looked at him, she felt herself treacherously wishing that Amanda had not come in just then. She was sure that whatever he might say, he was by no means indifferent to her, whether it be wholly physical or otherwise. 'Run along,' he said unkindly.

Susan walked swiftly to the door, conscious of his eyes following her. She looked at Amanda, but Amanda was watching Dominic, and she shrugged and moved out of the room.

'Yes, you go on,' said Amanda suddenly, looking at Susan. 'I want to have a word with Dominic.'

'All right,' Susan clasped her hands together. 'I'm rather tired. I think I'll go to bed.'

Dominic turned his back on both of them and rising to his feet crossed to the wide fireplace and, producing a case of cigars, proceeded to light one.

'That's right,' said Amanda, rather absently. 'I'll see you later. I'll look in on my way to bed.'

Susan nodded, and without speaking to Dominic she walked quickly along the corridor towards the hall.

Her thoughts were in a turmoil, and a sinking feeling heralded the depression which she knew must follow. There had been a forbidden exhilaration in the last few minutes, and now she was realizing the after-effects.

Meanwhile, Amanda had entered the kitchen and closed the door. Dominic turned slowly and saw her, and said:

'Spare me the lectures, Amanda. I know exactly what you are going to say.'

'Do you, now? Well, then, I won't bother to say it.'

'No. It won't be necessary.' He poured himself another goblet of the ruby wine and drank from it thirstily.

Amanda lit herself a cigarette, and then seated herself at the table where he had been sitting.

'Just why have you come here, then?' she asked abruptly.

Dominic shrugged. 'Something came up. I wanted to see Fay, if you must know.'

'And it couldn't wait?'

'I guess it might have waited a couple of days, why? Am I forbidden to come to my sister's house because you are here? Hell's bells, A.B., you're not my keeper. I can't understand you. I used to think you thought something about me; at least I was sure we were friends. After this inquisition, it makes me wonder what you really think!'

Amanda had the grace to look a little disturbed at his words, and she said quietly:

'If I'm acting out of character, it's simply that I don't want Susan hurt, and you know it. I know in the past few years, you have been unscrupulous where women are concerned. With women of your own set, it doesn't matter what you do. Most of them live for the thrill of affairs, both sordid and cheap, and they ask for everything they get. Susan is not like that, and I will not allow her to become embroiled with you, no matter what! You're too old for her, to begin with, and although I detest that young puppy she's got herself engaged to, I'd rather she married him and lived a monotonous life than become just another of your women!'

Dominic bit angrily on his cigar. 'What makes you think I'm the least bit interested in your "Susan"?'

'Well! Aren't you?'

Dominic gave a grim smile. 'All right, I do find her attractive. She's unusually refreshing. And rather naïve as to her own charms.'

'You see!' Amanda sighed.

Dominic removed the cigar from his mouth and said softly, 'I do have some self-control, you know.'

Amanda drew hard on her cigarette. 'Yes. And I won't say any more about it.'

'Good. I must confess the subject was beginning to bore me.'

Amanda looked at him shrewdly. 'All the same, Dom, you are used to getting what you want.'

'Within reason.' Dominic looked cynical. 'I didn't exactly make the grade with my wife, did I?'

'How is Veronica?' Amanda looked at him. 'Have you seen her lately?'

'Oh, yes, I've seen her. And I guess she's going along all right. She hopes to be out of the clinic by the summer.'

'I see. Dom, why don't you divorce her?'

Dominic crushed out his cigar against the stone wall of the fireplace.

'Would you kick someone when they were down?' he asked quietly.

'No. But that's hardly the case with you two, is it?' She sighed. 'Dom, she's not like an innocent creature who's been cruelly treated. She went into this of her own free will.'

Dominic shook his head. 'I don't believe that anybody does that,' he muttered. 'No one knows until they're hooked just what it really means. And by then it's too late. So, you see, Veronica might have been experimenting.'

Amanda shook her head. 'And what about the times she's gone back to drinking after she's been supposedly cured?'

'No one is ever cured. Alcoholics are temporarily on the wagon. But you must always remember, Amanda, that an alcoholic is only one drink away from addiction. That's the way it is with Veronica, and she doesn't have the strength to resist or want to.' He laughed without mirth. 'Oh, A.B., have you any idea how she looks to-day, compared to what she used to be? Do you remember when we got married, how lovely she was then? Now she's just a slave to the habit. Her eyes dart here and there when you're talking to her. She's as thin as a rake and twice as pallid. She hardly eats at all; she's just a bag of nerves. How can you ask me to divorce her, whatever she's done to me?'

'So you still love her?' Amanda said wonderingly.

'Love!' Dominic closed his eyes for a moment. 'Oh, God, I don't love her any more!' He sounded incredulous. 'What do you think I am? I pity her, God, how I pity her, but love! No, A.B., there's no love involved. She killed any feelings I had for her years ago. My love died when I came home from a business trip

84

twelve years ago and found her in bed with another man.'

He shrugged dismissively. 'No one knows about that! I think Fay guessed. She knew what was going on, but didn't want me to get to know by hearsay. She knew I would find out for myself when I got home, and I did! God, I got out of the house like a mad thing! If I'd stayed I think I would have strangled her!'

'Then why didn't you divorce her then?'

'Well, because of Jon. He was only a baby. I misguidedly thought he would be better with his mother than with me. How wrong I was! When I took him away from her she didn't even know he'd gone. She'd been practically unconscious for three days. The maid had been taking care of him. I called the hospital and they took her away. Afterwards she went to live in America.'

Amanda felt nauseated. 'And how old was Jon, then?'

'Seven. I'm afraid he hasn't a very high opinion of his mother.'

'And rightly so. Honestly, Dominic, you've been too soft with her. You should have divorced her years ago.'

'But why? I'll never marry again. Don't worry, A.B. I have no intention of going through this again.'

'That's ridiculous, Dominic. There are very few women who go off the rails in such a manner. Veronica is not quite normal.'

'Do you think she's unique? Because I can assure you she is not. The clinic where she is at the moment is full of females like her, women who are not satisfied with their husbands, or who for some reason or another can't find the satisfaction in life they crave for.'

'I know. But, Dom, any normal girl—'

Dominic raised his hand. 'I'm seriously considering buying an island in the West Indies and taking myself off there. The lotus-eating life would suit me fine.'

85

'You'd never do it! You're much too involved with your work.'

Dominic smiled. 'You're half right. At the present time, I think work provides me with the perfect sedative.'

'Oh, Dominic, I wish there was something I could do for you!'

Dominic raised his shoulders, and then opening his cigar case, he said, 'If you're serious, there is something you can do.'

'What?'

He frowned. 'I'm beginning to think that Jon is rather too advanced for his age and I think I'm to blame. He's not getting sufficient opportunity to be himself. Even at school, I'm told, he's an introvert. How would you like to spend a month with him on the *Ondine*?'

'The yacht?'

'Sure. You could write there, just as well as at home. It's at present lying off a resort called Delice along the coast from Monte Carlo. It's wonderful there at this time of year, and the yacht is well equipped to cater for only three people. You, Jon and Miss Stacey.'

Amanda frowned. 'Dominic!'

Dominic groaned. 'For goodness' sake, A.B., I won't be there. I'm asking this for Jon, and for no one else. I shall be leaving for New York within the next week. That's why I've come to see Fay instead of waiting until next weekend. I'll be away for some time. Jon expects to return to school in a week or so, anyway, but I'll get in touch with the school and defer his return indefinitely. I'm not satisfied with leaving it until the summer. He's getting older all the time. And anyway, as you've pointed out, Susan is a very young person, and she will make him an ideal companion.'

'Oh, Dom, why can't Miss Carruthers go with him, and you could send Fay's children too. They would make good companions for him.'

Dominic shook his head. 'I disagree. He doesn't get along with Yvonne and Jeremy very well. That's why I always hesitate to send him here. He didn't want to come in the first place, and I feel as though I'm neglecting him.'

'You are.'

'All right. But I can't change my plans overnight. I have to go abroad and that's that.'

Amanda hesitated. She was torn between a desire to help both Jon and Dominic, and her concern for Susan's apparent attraction towards Dominic.

'And if I agree to go, you won't turn up every week-end, expecting to be entertained?' she asked shrewdly.

Dominic smiled. 'No. If you like, I'll stay away.'

Amanda sighed. 'Perhaps you'd better. Although Jon is bound to wonder why you aren't visiting us.'

'He won't if I'm abroad. He never expects to see me during term time.'

'Well, I still don't know. After all, I have to ask Susan, and quite honestly, I can't see that young man of hers agreeing to this.'

'Hell, I'd almost forgotten him.' Dominic looked annoyed. 'Well, if you can't, you can't, and that's that.'

Amanda grimaced. 'Stop sounding so martyred. You know if I can take him, I will. And Susan seems to like Jon too. I noticed when we came over on the plane that they got along excellently together.'

Dominic loosened the top button of his shirt. 'Good,' he murmured, but his eyes were a little thoughtful, and Amanda found herself wishing that life was not quite such a fateful affair.

CHAPTER SIX

SUSAN did not see Dominic again before they left for Paris next morning, although she found her eyes looking for him all the while their cases were being loaded into the car, and good-byes were being said. She was genuinely sorry to leave Jon. He had assumed his shell of indifference, but she could tell that he really wished they were not leaving. Susan had had to agree that Yvonne and Jeremy were nice children, but definitely very young for their ages, and with them Jon felt doubly at a disadvantage. She wished she had not said what she had to Jon's father the previous evening. If she had not blown up like that, she might have been able to persuade him that Jon did require a different environment from the one he was living in now. Somewhere where he could relax completely, and be himself, without feeling he was being watched either by younger or older inquisitors.

To her surprise, Amanda said that they would be returning to England that afternoon, instead of waiting until Monday as planned.

'I managed to get word through to the airport,' said Amanda, taking her cigarettes out of her handbag, 'and we've been booked on a flight leaving at four o'clock.'

'Have we?' Susan raised her eyebrows. 'Why? Are you wanting to get back to work?'

'No, not at all.' Amanda ran a tongue over her lips. 'Actually, darling, I have something to ask you. I came to your room last night, after you left me with Dominic downstairs, but you were asleep.'

Susan flushed scarlet, and hoped Amanda would not realize that she had merely been pretending to be asleep to avoid the inevitable questioning.

'Please, Amanda,' she said, 'don't let's talk about

88

Dominic Halstad.' She twisted her gloves uncomfortably. 'I know what you're going to say, so please spare me the monologue.'

Amanda looked abashed. 'It seems to me that everybody thinks they know what I'm going to say before I say it myself,' she said sharply. 'You're wrong, Susan, if you think I'm going to warn you against Dominic. I've already done that, without a great deal of success, it seems.'

'Oh, Amanda!'

'Well, anyway, I won't say anything else about that just now. What I want to say, you may find entirely unsuitable to you.'

Susan frowned, intrigued now to know what it was. 'Go on, then. I'm all ears, and dying to know,' she remarked dryly.

'It's simply this: how would you like to spend a month on a yacht lying in the bay of Monte Carlo?'

Susan was astonished, and looked it. Never had she imagined such a question. It was fantastic!

'You must be joking,' she said, looking curiously at her employer. 'Why should I want to do that, in the first place?'

'In the first place because Dominic has asked me to take Jon there, and in the second place because I need you as my companion, and helper, and also as a playmate for Jon.' Amanda finished rather quickly, and was not surprised when Susan said at once:

'But what about David?'

'Exactly. What about David? I suppose it's too much to expect that he would agree.'

'Much too much,' said Susan, nodding. 'I'm sorry, Amanda, but it's out of the question.'

'M'm, I thought you'd say that. Pity!'

'But I still don't understand. Why should Dominic want to send Jon there, and with *us*?'

Amanda noticed the easy way Dominic's name rolled

off Susan's tongue, and she gave a little sigh. Then she said:

'Well, for some reason, Dominic has suddenly realized that Jon is being deprived of the easy companionship of youth. He's realized that Jon is becoming an introvert, apart from when he's with his father, and that he needs a complete break from routine. I agree with him.'

'And so do I!' exclaimed Susan, clasping her hands together, her eyes suddenly bright. So he had taken notice of what she had said after all!

'So there you are then. The chance to do something for Jon, and a wonderful holiday into the bargain. What more could any girl ask for?'

'Oh, I know, Amanda, and I'd absolutely adore to go, but you know what David will say.'

Amanda bit her lip solemnly. 'It seems to me, Susan, that you and your fiancé are drifting apart.'

'Whatever do you mean?'

'You say you would love to spend a month away from David, and then say that he would never let you. Surely, if you love him as you say you do, you couldn't bear the thought of a whole month without seeing him.'

Susan pressed her lips together for a moment. She didn't want to admit it, but of course Amanda was right. She ought not to feel this way, And she ought not to think about Dominic Halstad all the time as she was doing at present. Even the prospect of spending some time with his son was infinitely more desirable than remaining in London with David.

It must be the glamour that surrounds this family, she thought, trying to excuse herself. She prayed that she was not falling in love with Dominic Halstad. If she did, the rest of her life would be just so much wasted time, for obviously any interest he might have in her was purely transitory, and after satisfaction he would turn elsewhere for diversion.

'Oh, Amanda,' she exclaimed desperately, 'do you really think I don't love David?'

Amanda hesitated. 'Look, child,' she said kindly, 'your destiny is your own affair. But, as sure as I am that association with Dominic Halstad would end in sorrow, I find the prospect of you spending the rest of your life longing for your freedom just as abhorrent. Last night I thought that David was the only solution to your problem. Now I'm not so sure.'

'Why?'

'Perhaps because whatever his faults, I love Dominic, and what he's doing with his life is not exactly what it seems. We talked for a long time last night, Dom and I, and he made me realize that it's fatally easy to judge a person's motives when you don't trouble to find out the true cause.'

Susan shrugged. 'Just now I can't even think about Dominic Halstad,' she said quietly. 'Do you think I ought to break my engagement?'

'Only you can decide that,' said Amanda. 'What you've got to ask yourself is, am I marrying David because I love him, or because he provides a chance for me to have a home of my own? Your orphanage background must have meant something in your life. Perhaps you're subconsciously searching for security.'

'You could be right,' said Susan slowly. 'But I always thought I loved David. I mean, I've known him long enough to be sure.'

'All right, then. Marry him and be done with it.'

Susan looked troubled. 'Perhaps if I went away with you for this month, it might help me to get things into perspective,' she said suddenly. 'What do you think?'

Amanda nodded slowly. 'Ye . . .s, perhaps it would, at that. If you explained to David that you were having this uncertainty, perhaps he would agree with you.'

'I doubt that, but never mind. I'll ask him. Yes, I'll ask him.'

On Sunday evening, Susan set off for the Chalmers' home feeling rather as though she were keeping an appointment with the dentist. It was not going to be easy telling David what she had decided, and it would not help if she could not speak to him alone until he was taking her home. Then she would have to rush the words and would most likely end up in tears.

If only Mrs. Chalmers could be out for once, so that they could spend a little time alone together. She needed assurance at this time, and only David's arms and lips could give it to her.

To her disappointment, Mrs. Chalmers herself answered the door to her knock, and looked surprised at the sight of Susan.

'So you're back,' she said uncompromisingly. 'And not before time.'

'Why? Is anything wrong?'

'Nothing much. Unless you consider David's near-pneumonia something.'

'Pneumonia!' Susan went pale. 'Where is he? Let me see him.' She pushed past Mrs. Chalmers and into the house. She started up the stairs and Mrs. Chalmers shouted:

'Don't you go up to his bedroom. It's not fitting.'

'Fitting! Fiddlesticks!' snapped Susan, regardless, and ran on up the staircase.

She knew the whereabouts of David's room and opening the door gently she went in. David did indeed look pale as he lay there, breathing hoarsely, and Susan put a hand to her throat feeling guilt exuding from her.

'David?' she murmured tentatively, and he opened his eyes.

'Susan! You're back! What are you doing here? I thought you were away until tomorrow.'

'Amanda came back a day early, dear. How do you feel?'

'Not so bad. It's just a severe cold. I'm a little wheezy, that's all . . .'

Susan stared at him. 'But your mother gave me to understand that it was pneumonia,' she began, in astonishment.

'So it might have been, for all you cared,' said Mrs. Chalmers' voice, from the doorway.

Susan rose from her position by the bed. 'Don't be ridiculous,' she said clearly, anger taking the place of guilt. 'David was perfectly all right when I left on Friday.'

Mrs. Chalmers shrugged her bony shoulders. 'All I know is that I've had an invalid on my hands since you left,' she retorted coldly.

'An invalid! If all he's got is a severe cold, then I imagine it must be your idea that he stays in bed. Good heavens, it's beautifully fresh outside. The fresh air would have done him more good than being cooped up here breathing all his germs over again.'

'I did feel rather ill,' said David's rather plaintive tones.

'Of course you did,' said his mother placatingly. 'Susan has never known a mother's love. She wouldn't understand how I felt when I found you poorly on Saturday morning.'

Susan felt stifled. Gone was her chance to speak to David. Even if his mother did leave them alone, which seemed unlikely in the circumstances, this did not seem like a good time to broach the subject of a trial separation.

She sighed, and said, 'Do you think David and I could be alone for a while, Mrs. Chalmers? I have rather a lot to say to him.'

Mrs. Chalmers folded her arms. 'David doesn't want to be talking a lot,' she said. 'His throat is sore and inflamed.'

Susan clenched her fists. 'I don't think a few words with me will overtax his strength.'

Mrs. Chalmers shook her head. 'The doctor said he should have rest and quiet.'

Susan tried to keep her temper. 'David,' she appealed to him, 'couldn't you manage a few words to me?'

David smiled, and gave a rather helpless shrug. 'Well, darling, can't it wait? I mean, after all, I didn't expect you back today, did I?'

Susan let her breath out in a whistle, and nodded her head in resignation.

'All right, David. Can I make an appointment to see you?'

David looked a little uncomfortable. 'Don't be silly, Susan. Come back tomorrow. I should be up by then.'

Susan looked from Mrs. Chalmers to David, and then back to his mother again.

'Very well, I'll come tomorrow at seven-thirty. But I want to see you alone. And that's a promise.'

David frowned. 'Is something wrong?'

Susan smiled rather cruelly. 'You'll have to wait until tomorrow to find out, won't you?' she said, with feeling.

However, on Monday morning, Susan received a telephone call from David's mother while she was at work. She was informed that Monday was not convenient for her to call round as the vicar from the nearby church had promised to come and see David and give him a game of chess and Susan would merely be in the way. Susan doubted whether David knew just what his mother had planned, but just at present she did not much care. She merely acquiesced and said she would come on Tuesday evening instead. She was determined to see David some time that week, but as he had been out of sorts perhaps the longer their talk was delayed the more receptive he might be.

Amanda, who had overheard the call, remarked that David's mother seemed capable of running David's affairs for him, and that perhaps Susan ought to bring the matter up with her instead of with David.

'Oh, Amanda, that's not very nice,' said Susan, frowning, although she could not help but feel that there was something in what Amanda said.

On Tuesday, Amanda had to go out in the morning to see her agent. She usually went to his office when they had business to discuss and Susan was left at rather a loose end.

She tidied her desk, answered a couple of letters and then asked Sarah whether she could make some coffee.

'Don't be silly,' exclaimed Sarah briskly. 'I'll make you some. You go and find something to fill your time and I'll bring it to you when it's ready.'

'Oh, thank you, Sarah, you're a darling!'

'Away with you, then, before I change my mind.'

Sarah chuckled, and Susan walked back through to the lounge. She lifted a copy of *The Tatler* and flicked idly through its glossy pages. There were photographs of well-known personalities who had attended a luncheon at the Dorchester the previous week, and Susan found herself looking at a picture of Dominic Halstad. He was photographed with Lord Amesley, and was smiling at something his companion had said.

Susan's hands trembled a little at the sight of him, and she swiftly turned the page. Of all people to see it had had to be him. It was as though fate was conspiring to make something of their association.

The doorbell rang and, calling 'I'll get it' to Sarah, Susan went to open the door. She almost gasped when she found the subject of her thoughts standing on the threshold.

He nodded rather coolly at her, and said, 'Is A.B. available?'

Susan gathered her scattered wits. 'I – er – no. She's gone out for the morning, to see her agent – ' She stopped speaking and ran a tongue over her dry lips. 'Er – won't you come in?'

Dominic hesitated. 'I don't think so,' he began slowly. 'I wanted to see Amanda herself. Do you know whether she's decided anything about the proposed trip?'

Susan clenched her fists. 'This is ridiculous,' she said quickly. 'Standing talking on the step like this. Please come in!'

Dominic shrugged, and stepped inside, as she stepped back to allow him to do so. Susan closed the door and, rubbing her hands together nervously, she preceded him into the lounge.

Dominic stood in the centre of the floor. Today he was wearing a light-blue suit and a sheepskin car-coat, and Susan couldn't help but notice how well his clothes fitted him. It was as though his tailor found delight in keeping him permanently well turned out.

Sarah appeared from the kitchen, a tray of coffee in her hands, and said:

'Oh, it's you, Mr. Halstad, sir! I'll get another cup.'

'Yes, do,' said Susan, nodding, and walking rather jerkily over to the table whereon the tray had been set.

'Cream?' she asked, looking at him.

'No. Black, with no sugar,' he said easily. 'May I sit down?'

'Please do.' Susan indicated a low chair and he sat down, stretching his long legs out in front of him. He accepted the cup of coffee Susan handed him, and produced his cigar-case. 'Do you mind?'

'No. Go ahead.' Susan perched on the side of Amanda's desk and lit herself a cigarette, drawing on it deeply. The nicotine temporarily soothed her nerves and she was grateful.

Dominic's expression was wry, as he said, 'We're so polite today, aren't we?'

Susan felt her cheeks beginning to grow hot. 'I think it's simply that we were rude the last time we met,' she replied, as calmly as she was able. 'It's very cold out today, don't you think?'

Dominic put down his coffee-cup and rose to his feet restlessly.

'You didn't answer my question,' he said. 'Has Amanda made a decision as to whether she is going to spend that month on the yacht?'

Susan swallowed hard. 'Actually she has. She says if I will go then it's all settled.'

'I was aware of something like that,' he said, sighing. 'And what about you? Are you going?'

Susan bit her lip. 'I don't know yet.'

'Have you asked your fiancé?'

'No, not yet. I'm seeing him tonight. I'll be able to give you an answer tomorrow.'

'Good. You will understand that there are arrangements to be made.'

'Yes, I understand. I'll definitely let you have an answer in the morning.'

Dominic nodded, and walked slowly across to the window, looking broodingly down on the city below.

'Tell me,' he said, his voice suddenly deeper, 'aren't you curious to know why I came to the apartment instead of ringing A.B. up?'

Susan stiffened her shoulders. 'No. Should I be?'

Dominic swung round and leaned against the window ledge. 'Damn you, yes,' he said, anger only partially concealed in his voice.

'All right, then, why?' she asked, looking at him rather cautiously.

Dominic chewed on his cigar, and then took it out of his mouth and studied the glowing tip with concentration.

'Well, because I wanted to see you,' he said, looking at her suddenly through eyes which were veiled by the thick lashes.

Susan slid off the desk with a bump, and turned away from him.

'I – I understand you're leaving shortly for the United States.'

'That's right. But you're changing the subject again. Are you scared?' He laughed a little scornfully. 'Little mouse!'

Susan swung round to face him. 'Why are you always baiting me?' she asked angrily.

'Isn't that usually what cats do with mice?' he mocked her. 'And it amuses me watching you get angry.' His smile was deliberately taunting. 'You'd love to be able to get your own back, wouldn't you?' he asked teasingly.

Susan seethed. As usual he was right. At the moment she felt she wanted to fling herself at him and torture him physically as he was torturing her mentally.

'And I'll tell you something else,' he continued. 'The reason you're getting so angry is because you wanted to see me just as much as I wanted to see you, didn't you?'

Susan felt breathlessly as though she had been running up a flight of stairs and upon reaching the top had been punched in the solar plexus.

'I can't imagine how you can have reached that conclusion,' she said, trying to keep calm.

'Can't you? Isn't it true, then?'

Susan straightened her back. 'No, it's not true.'

Dominic straightened up also, his eyes dangerously bright. 'Just for once,' he muttered, 'admit it. Admit I'm right.'

Susan's nerves felt as taut as violin strings. 'I – I can't,' she said, bending her head.

98

Dominic walked across to her, and lifted her chin with one hand so that she was forced to look at him.

'I wonder why,' he murmured slowly, so that Susan could hardly hear his words. 'You're not really beautiful and, as Amanda said, you're very young and very naïve.'

'Please,' said Susan. 'Mr. Halstad, please!'

Dominic did not release her. 'The name is Dominic,' he said quietly. 'Say it.'

Susan stared at him, her eyes wide and bemused.

'My name; say it!' he commanded softly.

'Dominic,' she said at last. 'Dominic.'

'I am right. Aren't I?'

'About what?'

Susan hesitated, and clenched her fists tightly.

'Goddammit, you know,' he muttered.

'I only know you're married,' she said shakily. 'And anything you find interesting in me is only a passing diversion.'

'You think so?'

'Of course. Amanda said —'.

'To hell with what Amanda said. I only know that since I met you out there,' he nodded towards the kitchen, 'I haven't had a minute's peace.'

'I don't have affairs,' said Susan, trying to maintain her dignity.

Dominic released her chin so roughly that it hurt. 'And I do.' He thrust his cigar into his mouth. He shook his head and turned away. 'I imagine Amanda has told you that I sleep with every woman that comes my way.' He sighed heavily. 'Amanda is apt to let her imagination get the better of her sometimes. She's a spinster herself, and I believe she's still a virgin, so she would be the best judge on matters of that sort.'

Susan put her hands on her hips. 'Oh, Dominic,' she exclaimed, in exasperation, 'why are you talking to me like this?'

99

He shrugged. 'I don't know.' He half-smiled. 'I guess my pride won't allow me to accept that you don't really find me attractive. After all, I am old enough to be your father, aren't I?'

'Hardly,' remarked Susan dryly. 'Although with you, it's just possible.' She found relief in being flippant.

He had to grin at this, and the tension relaxed. Susan prayed she could remain this unconcerned.

'Well, I guess that's all, then,' said Dominic, after studying her for an agonizing moment. 'I'll go. If you do decide to go with A.B. don't worry that I shall be turning up every other day. I won't.'

'All right. I'll tell Amanda you called.'

'Yes, do. She'll be horrified to learn that you've entertained me here without a chaperon.'

His tone was sardonic and Susan walked swiftly to the door and opened it. 'Good-bye, Mr. Halstad.'

'Good-bye, Miss Stacey.'

He walked past her out of the door and then halted. 'Well, well, A.B. You're just in time to see me go.'

Amanda appeared from the direction of the lift. She looked a little perturbed and he said:

'I've been adequately looked after by your inestimable secretary. And she's been able to tell me all about the whys and wherefores of your proposed sojourn on the *Ondine*.'

'Is that all?' asked Amanda.

'Absolutely,' said Dominic lazily. 'Good-bye, A.B. Good-bye – Susan.'

'Good-bye, Mr. Halstad.' Susan went back into the apartment and after a moment Amanda followed her.

'How long has he been here?' asked Amanda at once.

'I don't know. Fifteen . . . maybe twenty minutes.'

'I see. And why did he come?'

Susan flushed. 'To see me, if you must know. And I'm glad he did. We've managed to sort out our affairs very satisfactorily, and I don't think you need worry any more. I think I can handle Mr. Halstad myself.'

Amanda eyed her rather sceptically, but did not comment. She thought Susan's words were a little foolhardy, but it was not her business really, whatever Susan chose to do with her life.

CHAPTER SEVEN

Susan had her interview with David on Tuesday evening as planned. Mrs. Chalmers herself had succumbed to the chill that had overtaken her son, and when Susan arrived at Medlar Grove she found David in the throes of preparing his mother a meal, while Mrs. Chalmers had had to retire to her bed.

Whisking David out of the kitchen, Susan whipped up a fluffy omelette for his mother, and after preparing a tray with a pot of tea and a little buttered toast, she told David to take it up to his mother while she prepared something for them.

She found some chops and tomatoes, as well as a few onions and mushrooms in the larder and in no time at all she was preparing a mixed grill with fried potatoes and curried beans. She piled David's plate with the steaming concoction and then carried it into the living-room where David had had the good sense to lay the table.

Having only a chop and a few mushrooms herself, she carried hers in and joined him at the table. David was munching enthusiastically and said:

'I say, Susan, you're a super cook!'

The boyish adjective epitomized everything David stood for, and with deliberation she said:

'David. If I were to go away for a month within the next few days, I mean – well, suppose we were separated for a month – would you mind?'

David stopped chewing and simply stared at her in astonishment.

'You must be joking,' he exclaimed when he had emptied his mouth.

'No, I'm not. It's just that lately I've been wondering about us.'

'What about us?'

'Well, you know yourself we've been having a lot of arguments about getting a home of our own, and it's made me wonder whether we're entirely suited to one another.'

David was obviously flabbergasted. 'You can't be serious,' he gasped. 'We – we're engaged!'

'I know we are. And I don't want to break the engagement, not unless you feel you can't let me go any other way, but I feel I need a chance to get things into perspective —'

'Get what into perspective? It's that Amanda Blake, isn't it? She's been poisoning your mind against me, hasn't she?'

'No. No, she has not. Look, David, don't you ever have any doubts about us?'

'Of course not. I love you. You're my girl.'

Susan sighed. It was harder than she had thought. 'Very well then, will you let me go abroad with Amanda for a month?'

'Where abroad?'

Susan felt nervous suddenly. 'Mr. Halstad wants Amanda to take his son down to the yacht for a few weeks, to allow him a break from routine. He's a very lonely boy, and he needs a chance to be brought out of himself—'

David thrust his plate to one side, and Susan noticed

that for all he was upset, he had managed to eat every-thing she had cooked for him.

'These Halstads have suddenly become very important in your Amanda's life, haven't they?'

'I suppose so. Look, David, if you could meet Jon you would realize for yourself what I mean.'

David was obviously grappling with his thoughts. 'Hell, I don't know what to think. What will Mother say?'

'It's nothing to do with your mother.' Susan sighed deeply. 'Good heavens, David, what can it possibly have to do with her? You see, this is what I mean. If you ask me, your mother rules your life for you, and if you expect me to put up with it, if and when we get married, you're mistaken. It's only for your sake that I hold my tongue now. Don't you see what she's doing to us?'

David straightened his shoulders. 'You must realize, Susan, that I love my mother. You can't understand that, can you, never having had a mother of your own?'

'Oh, God,' groaned Susan, 'you're even beginning to sound like her!'

David frowned. 'I don't consider that a fitting thing to say here, with my mother lying ill upstairs and unable defend herself.'

'All right. I'll go.' Susan rose to her feet. She had barely touched her meal. She reached for her coat, and pulled it on quickly. She wanted to get out of that house as soon as possible. She couldn't breathe in its torpid atmosphere.

'Now wait a minute!' David moved forward. 'You can't just leave like that. What are you going to do?'

'I'm going to go with Amanda,' said Susan firmly, feeling dangerously near to tears. Too much was happen-ing all at once and it was becoming too much for her to stand. The break would definitely do her good. She was rapidly coming near to a state of depression.

David thrust his hands into his trousers pockets, and looked thoughtful.

'Well,' he said, as she buttoned her coat and picked up her handbag, 'I think you're going to regret this.'

'I doubt it,' retorted Susan, biting her lips to stop them from trembling. 'Here's your ring, David. I'll leave it with you. Just in case your mother decides that she can't let our engagement continue.'

'Now, Susan —' he began.

'No, don't say anything. It's what I expected. But if you do want to see me after I get back, contact me, and we'll discuss it then.'

David looked stern. 'I must make it clear that if you walk out of that door without my ring we're finished,' he said, giving her an ultimatum.

'Very well, David,' she said. 'If that's the way you want it, there's nothing more to be said.'

David was taken aback. He had not expected Susan to be so complacent. He had expected her to come back to him, begging for his forgiveness.

'Now look here!' exclaimed David. 'Don't let's do anything we're both likely to regret. You know I love you, whatever I may say or do, and my mother is only doing and saying what she thinks is right. You must admit, her point about this house is not entirely unreasonable.'

Susan sighed deeply. 'Not to you, maybe, David, but, as you're continually pointing out, I've never had a home of my own and the prospect of having a home which is already dominated by your mother is not particularly enticing to me. Perhaps I'm being unreasonable. I'm not sure. But I'm sure that if we live with your mother, she'll do her utmost to make me look an idiot, and make you wish you'd never married me.'

'That's nonsense!'

'No, it's not. Good heavens, David, surely you can see that it would never work?'

'I can see that you're building it up into something disastrous. You're making my mother an excuse for breaking the engagement, if you ask me.'

Susan gave an involuntary gesture. 'Perhaps I am,' she agreed. 'At any rate, David, I need a little time to be sure. These past couple of weeks I've become unsettled. It's stupid, I know, but I can't help it. I think, to a certain extent, my desire for a home and a family has been overriding my natural desires. I love you, David, but perhaps not in quite the way I should.'

'I bet that creature Amanda Blake has something to do with this!' David sounded furious.

'She hasn't; at least not directly. On the contrary, she has said that I'm behaving rather foolishly. Oh, David, couldn't you agree to me going to Delice? It's only a month, after all, and when that's over we may find we are ready to start afresh.'

David thrust his hands deeper into his pockets. 'I don't know what to say. Of course, I can't stop you if you've made up your mind, but I do think you're being rather hasty. A trip to a luxury yacht does sound enticing, I admit, but that's all it is, you know, just a trip!'

'I know. What are you trying to say?'

David straightened his shoulders. 'I think you've become infatuated with Dominic Halstad!'

Susan stared at him in amazement.

'You see! You don't deny it!'

Susan shrugged. 'If I did, you wouldn't believe me. Besides, I'm not altogether sure you're not right.'

'What! You must be crazy!' David had apparently not considered that what he was accusing her of might be the truth. 'It must be his money! It must be blinding you to everything else. He's married, isn't he?'

'Yes. He's married. But he doesn't live with his wife; at least I don't think he does.' Truth to tell, she did not know whether he did or not. The fact that he did not at the moment proved nothing. She was in a clinic for alcoholics. He could hardly live with her there.

David snorted angrily. 'The more I hear of this, the less I like it. Don't think I intend to be second to some useless playboy!'

Susan gasped, and then quickly turned and walked to the door.

'I think we've both said more than enough,' she spoke quietly. 'I'm going now. If you want to see me when I get back, ring me. Otherwise, I shall know it's over.' She placed his ring on the sideboard, and went swiftly along the gloomy hall and out of the door.

As always when she left Medlar Grove, she felt a sense of complete freedom again, doubled tonight by the knowledge of her broken engagement. She was not happy about it. Although she acknowledged to herself sub-consciously that she and David would never be able to make a go of things while his mother dominated him, the feeling that she was somehow more alone than ever sent shivers of apprehension down her spine, and she wondered what the future had in store for her now.

CHAPTER EIGHT

Ondine, the Halstad yacht, was even more delightful than Susan had imagined. Eighty feet in length, it was a graceful vessel, painted overall in gleaming white enamel, with the sun of the Mediterranean glistening on the chrome fittings, and wide picture windows. Amanda had told her that these windows were made of a special kind of glass which could withstand any amount of buffeting, and that when the yacht was at sea in rough weather, sitting in the cabin was an exciting adventure, the waves lashing against the panes.

Jon had met them at Nice airport and they had driven to the village of Delice where they had been escorted out to the yacht in a motor boat by the captain, Gregory MacMasters. Amanda knew the captain vaguely and Jon, of course, knew him very well. Jon was a different child from the rather solemn boy they had taken to Fontainebleau. He was obviously looking forward enormously to their holiday, and continually wore a smile.

He had been very pleased when he learned that Susan was accompanying them. He considered her only a little older than himself, and the fact that there were nine years between them was narrowed by Susan's spontaneous vitality.

Susan herself had decided to let things take their natural course, and refused to worry any longer about her emotional difficulties. Here, in an entirely new environment, she would be able to shed her former anxieties, and become as carefree as she should be.

Even Amanda seemed to have caught a little of their youthfulness, and had even gone so far as to buy herself a couple of linen dresses to wear while she was away.

From the yacht, looking back towards the shoreline, the vista was quite breathtaking. Whitewashed villas nestled among the hills above the bay, in gardens that were a mass of flowers.

The yacht was fitted with every kind of modern gadget. Susan's cabin had a foldaway bed, a writing bureau which could also be used as a table, an armchair which was fitted to the floor and the carpet was silver grey and luxurious. The armchair, and its matching counterpart in a dining-chair, were upholstered in red brocade, as was the headboard of the folding bed.

An adjoining bathroom had a small round bath, and a shower attachment which Susan made full use of during the warm weather. The taps again were silver and instead of a carpet on the floor, as had been the case in the Paris apartment, an intricate mosaic of various shades of green was cool to the feet.

The fitted wardrobe in the bedroom compartment was enormous, and Susan could only assume, as she hung away her own limited selection of clothes, that the usual occupants of the cabin had sufficient wardrobes to fill it. In her case, barely half the space was used, and she smiled rather wryly to herself as she slid shut the doors.

On the deck of the yacht there was a small swimming pool, filled with sea-water, that was continually being changed, as the water was pumped back into the sea by the same method as it was withdrawn.

Susan and Jon made full use of the pool, incessantly in the water when the sun was beating down. In no time at all, they were both tanned a golden brown, and Susan's hair seemed to bleach whiter than ever.

Within a week, the change in Jon was noticeable. He no longer made sardonic remarks and instead seemed to have emerged completely from his shell.

Amanda had not as yet started on a new novel, although she said there was one floating round in her brain, which would soon require attention. Susan had smiled at this, as she knew that Amanda would delay starting the novel as long as she could to allow Susan the freedom this holiday afforded.

It was strange to begin with, living on the yacht, continually feeling the gentle movement of the boat as it moved on the swell.

She rose to the sound of the lapping waves and the shrill cry of the sea-birds, and at night the movement of the water rocked her gently to sleep.

Captain MacMasters was a splendid storyteller, and during the long hot afternoons, when most people rested, Mac, as they called him, would come and sit beside the pool with his pipe, and tell them about his exploits during the war, and of how he was captured by the Germans and incarcerated in a prison camp. If the stories sounded a little like fiction sometimes, Jon would merely glance at Susan, and they would smile at one another, and listen just as attentively, for Mac was a born yarnspinner, and did not take offence when they chided him for his vivid imagination.

The staff on the yacht were young in the main, and treated Susan no differently from Jon and Amanda, but Susan felt rather self-consciously aware that she was merely a secretary and ought not to be treated as anything else.

When she broached the subject with Amanda, she merely laughed, and said:

'Oh, Susan, you are old-fashioned! Do you honestly imagine that your background makes any difference here? Good heavens! You're a guest of Dominic's just as much as I am, and will be treated as such.'

Susan shrugged, and had to acquiesce. Besides, it was very pleasant to be waited on for a while. But she could quite see that over a period the experience might begin to pall.

One afternoon, Amanda went down to her cabin for a rest as usual, and Susan and Jon stretched out side by side on one of the airbeds that were strewn rather haphazardly beside the pool. They were both in swimming costumes, Susan's of vivid white accentuating the tan of her skin.

Jon was silent for a while and then he said, suddenly, 'Tell me, Susan, do you know about my mother?'

Susan propped herself up on one elbow and looked down at him.

'Yes, I know. Your aunt told me, actually. Why?'

Jon sighed and shook his head. 'I wanted to talk to you about it.'

Susan frowned, 'In what way? I can't see how I can be of any use.'

'Well, you can. You see, if I talk about Mother with Dad, he seems to clam up on me, and not want to talk about it, and all Amanda can say is "It's none of your business!" Well, it is! And I want to talk about it to somebody, and you're the only person I've ever met whom I could really talk to, apart from Dad. And, in this case, as I've just said, Dad won't talk.'

'But what do you want to talk about?'

Jon shrugged. 'I don't really know. Only I haven't seen my mother for years, and now that I'm fifteen, I think I should.'

'Does she want to see you?'

'I don't think so. I remember, when I was little, she used to be a very beautiful lady with long red hair, and greenish-grey eyes. You've got green eyes, did you know that?' He smiled. 'Anyway, in those days, I thought she was marvellous. Oh, I know, I was brought up by a nanny, but when my mother came to say good night to me, she used to smell of perfume and be wearing the most gorgeous dresses. She didn't like me to kiss her when she was ready to go out. She said I would smudge her lipstick.'

Susan looked down at him in compassion. 'And did your father come to say good night, too?'

Jon looked embarrassed. 'I – well, I don't think she used to go out with Dad very often. There was a succession of uncles, I remember; Uncle Brad, Uncle Alan and Uncle Peter. I remember those three, but there were others.'

'And how do you feel about her now?'

'I don't know. I know she was a terribly bad wife and mother, but she is my mother when all's said and done, and I can't just not feel anything for her. She didn't even know, you know, that I'd been taken away from her.

She'd been in a stupor for about three days, so Dad said.'

Susan frowned. 'Do I take it that your father was not living with you at that time?'

'No. He left when he came back from a business trip and found that Mother had been unfaithful to him while he was away.'

'Oh!' Susan felt horrified. No wonder Dominic Halstad had such a low opinion of her sex. He had not had any of the pleasurable comforts of a contented home, and his wife had done her utmost to turn him into a cynic.

Jon looked at her rather sympathetically. 'You really are a very nice girl, aren't you?' he asked, in a tone that implied that 'a nice girl' was not a nice thing to be.

'I suppose that even living in an orphanage doesn't prepare you for this kind of thing,' she admitted slowly. 'You see, although I know my parents were never married, at least that's what Matron said to us, life in the home was rather strict and our upbringing was quite old-fashioned. We were taught never to trust the kind of man who – well, wanted an affair, whether his intentions were honourable or otherwise. We were told we should hold out for marriage, no matter what, and that marriage without love was preferable to bringing an illegitimate child into the world.'

Jon was interested. 'Go on,' he said, rolling on to his side, and cupping his head with his hand. 'Where did your parents come from?'

Susan smiled, and studied her toe-nails. 'That's the sixty-four-thousand-dollar question,' she replied, rather sadly. 'I do know my mother was a nurse, from Ireland, and my father was reputed to be a fellow student, but it couldn't be proved for me, and my mother died soon after I was born. But she didn't want me any more than your mother wanted you, apparently. She left me at the home and had no intention of having me back. Her career was more important.' She looked at Jon. 'I was not adopted as most babies are today. Instead, I lived at the orphanage until I was sixteen, and then I came to London.'

'Poor you!' Jon smiled at her. 'I grumble an awful lot about my life, but compared to yours, it's really been quite acceptable, hasn't it?'

'Of course. And I think your father was right, taking you away if your mother was so uncaring. After all, what life would you have had with her, had you continued to tag after her?'

'She was taken into a nursing home,' said Jon, by way of reply. 'There was really no choice for me. Besides, Ruthie was more like a mother to me than Veronica. Veronica was just the fairy off the Christmas tree, who happened to live in our house.'

Susan lay back again. She could imagine the young Jon, youthfully romantic, picturing his mother as the most beautiful creature imaginable. To find that his idol had feet of clay must have come as quite a shock for him. Even today, talking like this, she could not tell exactly what he felt for Veronica.

Sometimes, in the evenings, Amanda and Susan would take the launch and go across to Monte Carlo. Although it was a thrilling experience for Susan, she found she was always glad to get back to the peace and tranquillity aboard the yacht, and said so to Amanda, one evening when they were sitting drinking coffee in a bistro near the Casino.

'I can't honestly believe that people who come here and do nothing else but gamble find it much of a holiday,' she said.

Amanda laughed. 'Darling, the people who gamble don't regard it as a holiday. Gambling can be a business or a drug, depending on who you are and how much you have to lose. But I see your point. Myself, I prefer the Bahamas for peace and relaxation. After all, what could be more apt than Paradise Island?'

Susan smiled. 'It does sound wonderful. That's where Nassau is situated, isn't it?'

'Yes. I think perhaps we might go to Nassau later in the year. I could write there. We could get a villa, and have a beach all to ourselves. Would you like that?'

Susan's face clouded. 'Amanda! You seem to forget entirely that I may be married later in the year.'

'I don't believe that. Not now. A girl can't break off her engagement one minute and put it on the next. When you broke with David, you broke because you didn't love him enough. If you had, trips to outlandish places, no matter how exotic, would have seemed secondary in comparison to your love for one another.' She shrugged her shoulders. 'Darling, you've got to get it into your head, sooner or later, David is not for you.'

Susan sighed. 'Then who is?'

'Perhaps you could find yourself a millionaire in Nassau. I hear the place is crawling with them.'

Susan giggled. 'Millionaires are usually fair, fat, bald and fifty.'

'Who told you that? Lots of American tycoons are much more attractive. And of course, Dom is a good example.'

Susan looked pointedly at her. 'I thought we agreed not to discuss Dominic Halstad!'

'So we did, love. I'm merely making an observation. Not discussing him. Anyway, I think we can safely dispense with Dom for other reasons. A, he's married, and B, he's forty and much too old for you.'

'In any case,' remarked Susan reasonably, 'he's hardly likely to marry again, is he? He seems utterly disenchanted with the whole female population. Apart from an occasional dabble in sex!'

Amanda roared with laughter. 'Oh, Susan, you really are funny! And you say the most unsuitable things with such an expression of detachment on your face that anyone would think you were talking about the weather.' She sobered. 'But you're right, of course. He said as much to me the other evening at Fay's. I don't think he will every marry again.'

Susan considered this possibility with as much detachment as she could. She reflected that she was a rather unworldly creature who had suddenly, as Jon said, been catapulted into a world of high society where morals were at a minimum, and where candour did not find much favour. Dominic Halstad, a married man of forty, was a typical product of this kind of society. Rich, well bred, cynical, attractive, but completely without conscience as regards women of his own kind. To a romantic like Susan, he represented all the things that she had hitherto found out of reach, and like everything that was out of reach it was doubly fascinating. Should the time ever come when such things were within reach, she felt sure she would find her feelings had changed and she would have no desire to pluck those forbidden fruits from the tree. She was sure she would have no idea how to handle a man like that, as witness the last time she had met him at Amanda's apartment. He had made mincemeat of her then, although she had maintained her distance, and had he attempted to make love to her, she felt she would have been absolutely terrified. She was silly and weak and ineffectual, and the sooner she acknowledged that fact the better it would be for all concerned. For all his faults, David was her kind of man, and with him she would not have to experience these doubts and uncertainties. She decided she would write home that evening, and ask him whether it would be possible for him to come to Nice for a weekend while she was on the yacht. She knew she could obtain leave from Amanda, and they could have a gay time, visiting a night club and maybe even trying their hand in the casino.

The decision made, she felt unutterably better, but she decided not to say anything to Amanda as she might try to change her mind.

She received a reply from David within a couple of days. The letter was delivered to the yacht with the rest of the mail, and Amanda handed her the letter looking rather questioningly at her.

'Is this David's handwriting?' she asked.

Susan swallowed hard. 'Yes,' she said defensively. 'Why?'

'I'm merely curious to know why he should be writing to you.'

'Well, if you must know, I wrote to him,' said Susan, definitely on her guard now.

Amanda shrugged. 'Did you now? Well, well! And what heart-pourings did you send to him?'

'No heart-pourings. I merely asked him whether he would like to come to Nice while I'm here, and spend a weekend here with me.' She looked defiantly at Amanda. 'I mean, of course, that we should stay at different hotels.'

'Of course.' Amanda was sarcastic, and Susan walked quickly away to her cabin, in order to read the letter in peace.

Once there, she tore open the envelope, and flinging herself on the bed she began to read:

'My dear Susan,

I am so glad that you have seen fit at last to write and in part apologize for your manner at our last meeting.'

Susan clenched her fists but continued:

'My mother, you will be happy to hear, has quite recovered from her illness, and is up and about again. The firm has just secured a contract to design a new

115

university building in the Midlands, and so as you can imagine this has boosted my salary quite considerably. So much so that our wedding will be one of the best ever.'

Susan compressed her lips. It was apparent that he considered her contention that all was not well between them as nothing of importance.

She read on, impatient now to know whether he was coming.

'Unfortunately, I will not be able to come to France while you are there. Apart from the fact that we are exceptionally busy at this time, Mother and I both consider such expense to be extravagant and unnecessary. You will be home in a little over a fortnight and we will be able to discuss anything that needs discussing then.

'This weekend Mother and I are going to redecorate my bedroom and I'm thinking of getting a fitted carpet there. Do you think green would be a good colour?'

Susan stopped reading. Her stomach was churning in earnest now. It seemed that, contrary to anything she had ever said, David was seriously considering living at his mother's house, if and when they should marry. Why else should he redecorate his room at this time and get a new *fitted* carpet? And why should he ask her about the colour?

She wanted to tear the letter into shreds to compensate a little for her disappointment. She had known he would consider the trip extravagant, but she had thought that he might come when things between them were in such a sorry state. She would willingly have shared the cost of the air fare with him, but he just disregarded her needs completely. Surely the letter she wrote to him explained most eloquently her feelings; her doubts and frustrations.

She read on to the end:

'Finally, let me know when you will be arriving back at the airport and I will come and meet you myself. It will be quite a reunion, and we won't ever part again. Until then,

All my love, darling,
David.'

Susan thrust the letter back into the envelope and stared moodily into space. As usual David made everything dull and prosaic. But then he was really quite a dull man, but she had been too wrapped up in other things properly to notice before. It wasn't until she met Dominic Halstad that the difference between men became so pointed, and she realized that David lacked the means of satisfying a woman completely. There was no magic with David, there never had been, and although it might seem stupid to some people, Susan felt sure there should be something more than a simple acceptance of one another. A woman needed to be cherished, and if David was like this now what would he be like in a few years' time when the first thrill of marriage had worn off?

She sat up dispiritedly, and rumpled her hair, looking at her sad reflection in the wardrobe mirror. Making a face at herself, she slid off the bed, and walking into the bathroom sluiced her face in cold water.

Feeling refreshed, she rubbed her skin thoroughly with the towel, bringing a tingle to her face. Then she returned to the bedroom and lit a cigarette.

She was leaning against the wall, looking idly through the window when there was a sudden banging at her door, and Jon burst in.

'I say,' he said, 'I'm sorry to barge in on you like this, but Amanda has had an accident!'

'What!' Susan stubbed out her cigarette immediately, and said, 'What happened? Where is she?'

Following Jon out of the cabin, they raced up the companionway to the deck.

'She slipped into the empty pool,' explained Jon as they went. 'Mac had had it drained for cleaning, you know, and Amanda just over-balanced and fell in.'

'Oh, good lord! Is she badly hurt?'

'I don't know. Mac has rung across for the doctor who attends us when we're down here, and we're just waiting now for him to arrive.'

'I see.' They emerged on deck and Susan hurried across to where Amanda was lying on some rugs. 'Darling! Are you all right? What on earth have you done to yourself?' She smiled reassuringly.

Amanda smiled a little in return, although she seemed to be in pain.

'Well, honey, I'm not quite sure what I've done. I feel as though I've broken every bone in my body.'

'But how did it happen? You're not usually so careless.'

Amanda grimaced. 'Never mind that now. I don't think you'll be able to spend that weekend in Nice, after all. I may have to spend a few days in bed and there's Jon . . .'

'Don't worry,' Susan smiled. 'I shan't be going to Nice anyway. David has declined my invitation.'

'He did?' Amanda sounded amazed.

'I'm afraid so. Why?'

Amanda shook her head. 'I'll explain later. Gosh, I hope that doctor arrives soon and gives me something. I feel dreadful.'

The doctor, who, Jon had explained, ran a clinic on the mainland, was a good-looking Frenchman and seemed to find Susan far more intriguing than his patient, although he handled Amanda expertly and seemed to know his job.

'I cannot say, without X-rays, of course,' he said, after

he had completed his examination, 'but I should imagine, Miss Blake, that you have fractured your ankle, and possibly your ribs are not all intact either. It will be necessary for you to be taken across to the clinic, where I can have the necessary tests made and keep you under observation for a couple of days.'

Amanda had obviously never even considered this contingency, for she began to protest volubly.

'But I can't possibly stay at your clinic,' she cried. 'Why, Jon and Miss Stacey would be left alone here on the yacht. I must return after the X-ray.'

Susan calmed her down. 'There's Mac,' she said, trying to pacify her. 'Surely he's capable of looking after the crew and us as well. Don't worry, Amanda. We can manage. Honestly!'

Amanda sighed helplessly. 'Oh, dear! I wish none of this had happened. I've been so silly!'

'Nonsense,' said Susan. 'Accidents will happen. So stop worrying and just concern yourself with getting back into the best of health again. If Doctor Gervaise says you must rest, you must rest. Do you want me to come with you now?'

'No, not at all. You stay here with Jon. After all, there's nothing you can do and the way I feel I shall probably be very irritable for a while.'

'Very well, I'll stay here. But please, Amanda, don't worry.'

Amanda was taken back to the shore in the launch with the doctor. They had telephoned from the yacht to the clinic and an ambulance was waiting on the quay for them. Susan watched her employer go with a feeling of anxiety. She hoped Amanda was not seriously incapacitated. She would become so restless if she was. And although it was a simple matter for Susan to take care of Jon on her own, she was rather concerned about his father's reactions if he should find out. Doctor Gervaise had told Susan, as Amanda was being lowered into the launch on a stretcher, that he suspected she might be a little concussed, and that it would definitely be necessary for her to rest in bed for two or three days at the least. Consequently Susan was aware, much more than Amanda, of her imminent responsibilities.

She wondered whether she ought to contact Dominic Halstad and inform him of the situation, but decided against it. He might consider her communication a plea for his assistance and knowing he was a busy man she did not want to trouble him. Besides, he would in all probability be in the United States at the present time and if this were the case it would merely cause him unnecessary concern.

Jon, over lunch, looked at things differently.

'I think we should contact Dad,' he said, as they ate a delicious shrimp cocktail from cut-glass dishes. 'He'll be annoyed if we don't.'

Susan took a sip of the wine they had as an aperitif, and said firmly:

'Why should he be annoyed about something that doesn't really concern him? Besides, Amanda may be back tomorrow.'

Jon looked sceptical. 'I heard what Gervaise said,' he replied. 'He doesn't expect her to be back before the weekend, now does he?'

Susan frowned. 'Jon, you seem to forget I'm twenty-four years old. I may act younger at times, but I can assure you that I'm quite capable of taking care of myself and you as well. Good heavens, in London, I share a flat with another girl and I'm often left on my own for days on end. And here we do have Mac and the rest of the crew.'

Jon shrugged. 'Mac's duties don't cover being in charge of me,' he remarked coolly. 'And anyway, why shouldn't I contact Dad myself? It's not really your affair, is it?' He sounded haughty, and Susan realized that for a moment he was reverting to the rather objectionable youth he had been that first time she met him at Amanda's flat.

She leant over the table towards him and said:

'Now you listen to me, Jon. Amanda has left me in charge!'

Jon looked astounded. 'Who do you think you're talking to?'

'You, my sweet young friend.' Susan allowed a smile at Jon's expression.

'You must be joking,' he said, almost choking over his food.

'No, I'm not exactly joking,' she replied. 'But I do think you should refrain from trying to exert any authority here. You're only here because Amanda agreed to bring you, and if anything serious has happened to Amanda, it's possible that we shall both be sent back to London at once when your father finds out.'

Jon's face dropped. 'Oh, lord, do you think so?'

'Well, it's not beyond the realms of possibility, is it? I mean your father is bound to think that we can't manage alone, just as Amanda does.'

'Yes, you're probably right.' He smiled in contrition. 'I'm sorry, Susan, if I sounded like a little prig.'

'That's okay. I suppose you were hoping your father might spend some time with you, weren't you?'

'Yes.' He sounded wistful. 'It would have been wonderful to see him for a while when he's not continually dashing here and there to conferences, and dinners, and cocktail parties and so on, as he does in London.'

Susan nodded. 'Never mind, Jon. I tell you what. Let's go into Monte this afternoon and do some shopping. I could do with some tights, and some more sun-tan cream. And of course,' she laughed, 'there're all the presents to buy for Delia and Sarah and Bill, back home. Quite an enormous amount, isn't it? Besides. I have a letter to post.' To David!

He chuckled. 'Oh, Sue, you are nice! After this holiday is over, I suppose I'll go back to that ghastly school, and you'll go back to being Amanda's secretary. By the way, are you going to get married later this year? Dad said you were.'

Susan raised her shoulders in an involuntary gesture. 'I don't really know,' she answered. 'I have a feeling that it's highly unlikely.'

CHAPTER NINE

THE following day, Susan visited Amanda at the clinic. She was lying in bed, propped up on pillows, but she looked very pale and Susan thought the fall must have shaken her more than she had thought.

'How do you feel, honey?' she asked gently, sitting down beside the bed on one of the deep armchairs provided. The clinic was very lushly equipped, and Susan thought that many of Doctor Gervaise's patients seemed to be middle-aged to elderly women, who apparently thought him wonderful. Having seen some of the patients walking about in extravagant *négligés* and beribboned housecoats, she had decided that many of their illnesses must be imaginary. They all looked perfectly fit to her.

She had said as much to the rather severe Scottish woman who was the Sister there, and had received the dour reply that women of uncertain age with an unlimited income found Doctor Gervaise's bedside manner more interesting than the casinos in the principality.

'Don't get me wrong,' she continued, in a broad brogue, as they walked down the corridor to Amanda's private room. 'Doctor Gervaise is an excellent doctor, but these women here, ach!'

Susan had chuckled a little. It must be frustrating for the Scottish Sister to suffer these foolish women when she genuinely wanted to treat the sick.

'Why do you stay, then?' she asked curiously.

The Sister smiled, 'Ah, well, Richard – Doctor Gervaise, you know, he's my nephew, and I suppose I'll have to stand by him or these women will eat him alive.'

Susan related this to Amanda, who smiled too. 'He really is terribly nice,' said Amanda, sighing. 'But I wish I could get out of this place. I'm absolutely bored stiff here, lying doing nothing. Where's Jon, by the way? You haven't brought him with you?'

'No. He wanted to come, but I persuaded him to stay with Mac. As far as I know he's helping him do whatever he does at this hour of the afternoon.'

Amanda smiled in relief. 'Good. I don't want the boy wandering round Monte Carlo unescorted.'

'Do you think I'm completely stupid?' exclaimed Susan dryly. 'Anyway, to get back to you, what does the doctor say?'

'To be quite honest, he doesn't say much at all. He had me X-rayed yesterday, and he's strapped up my ankle and my ribs. He says a couple of my ribs are cracked and my ankle is fractured. Hence the cage!' She indicated the mound beneath the bedclothes.

Susan shook her head. 'Honestly, Amanda, however did you do it?'

Amanda looked a little shamefaced. 'Well, Susan, I'll be honest with you; when you got that letter from David and you said you'd written and asked him out here I was very annoyed. I didn't like the idea of you running after that man. Anyway, I thought I would just slip, on the deck, and say I had sprained my ankle and take to my bed—'

'What!' Susan was amazed. 'Amanda, you didn't?'

'Yes. Well, I thought if I was incapacitated temporarily, you wouldn't be able to go to Nice. But I'm afraid I didn't realize that the pool was empty, and quite unknowingly I stepped on a greasy patch and pitched head first into the pool!'

'Oh, good lord!'

'Yes. You see, no good comes of being spiteful. This is simply retribution. Particularly as you came and said that David had refused your invitation after all. It was poetic justice, I think.'

Susan had to smile. She couldn't help herself.

'Amanda, really! You could have crippled yourself.'

'Do you imagine I had any idea this would ensue? My dear, if I could live yesterday again, you could go to Nice as far as I'm concerned. I wouldn't risk anything like this again for anybody.'

'So. But when do you really expect to get back?'

Amanda shook her head. 'I honestly don't know. Perhaps if you see the doctor as you're leaving you could ask him. I'd like to know myself. Whatever you say I don't like you and Jon alone on that yacht with only the crew for company. You're neither of you old enough to be left like that.'

'Oh, nonsense,' cried Susan. 'We're perfectly capable of being left alone. Don't concern yourself with us.'

'Have you had Mac contact Dominic?'

'Of course not. That's not necessary.'

Amanda grimaced. 'I must admit that I don't like the idea of Dom coming to stay with you any better than your being alone,' she remarked gloomily.

'Why not, for heaven's sake? Not that I want him to come, but you have no need to be worried. I can handle him should the need arise.'

Amanda shrugged. 'Perhaps you can, and perhaps you can't. But anyway, I don't really want to worry him. It may be that I'll be able to return in a couple of days. Surely he can't keep me here any longer.'

'Well, don't get any ideas about signing yourself out of the clinic,' said Susan reprovingly. 'You stay here and get completely cured.'

'All right, all right. I won't do anything foolish. But do take care, won't you, darling?'

'Of course. Now, is there anything you would like me to get for you?'

Susan saw the doctor as she left and asked him about Amanda's condition, but he was a little evasive.

'You see, Miss Stacey, I cannot give you any definite decision as yet. We must wait and see how she is in a couple of days, and then I might be able to tell you. She seems quite well in herself, but she is not a young woman and the bones of the ankle have been rather awkwardly fractured. It may be necessary for them to be reset, should they prove to be slow to knit. *Voilà*, your Miss Blake is a very active woman, am I not right?' Susan nodded. 'And if I allow her to leave here as soon as she thinks fit, she will not give her ankle the rest it needs. Besides, she has pain with the ribs, but she will not admit it. She shies against taking drugs.' He nodded. 'Yes, I am sure I am right to keep her a little longer.'

Susan had to be content with this and hoped that when the couple of days had elapsed, Amanda could be discharged in good condition.

She took a taxi back to Delice feeling quite extravagant, but consoled herself with the thought that the buses were slow and infrequent, and she was in charge of Jon when all was said and done.

She signalled the launch from the quayside and one of the crew members brought it across to collect her.

She climbed aboard and fanned herself with the outsize

sun-hat she had treated herself to in Monte Carlo, when she and Jon had gone shopping.

She was dressed in a slim-fitting dress of white linen with slits up the sides which she considered quite daring, although in the capital she had seen any number of dresses much, much more revealing than her own.

She was unaware of how attractive she looked, her skin golden and glowing with health, contrasting sharply with the whiteness of her dress and her shining hair. The man who was lounging lazily against the rail of the yacht watched her approach with interest, his eyes curiously intent for once as they looked on a woman.

Susan was not conscious of being scrutinized and when the launch reached the yacht and she looked up into Dominic Halstad's face she gave a surprised gasp.

'What on earth are you doing here?'

Dominic helped her aboard, his fingers hard and cool against her smooth flesh, and then he released her and said:

'That was *some* greeting! However, I'll ignore it for the time being. And as this is my yacht, and I have as much right here as anyone else, I don't think I really need to answer you, but I will.'

Susan spread wide her hands. 'If you've come because of Amanda, you needn't have taken the trouble. We're quite all right here.' She looked round for Jon. 'And when I get my hands on your son, I'll have a few words to say to him. I told him not to contact you.'

Dominic loosened the collar of his shirt, and pulled his tie down a little. 'Jon isn't the culprit,' he replied easily. 'Mac contacted me, as was his duty to do so. I told him to advise me every few days of any mishaps.'

'Oh, you did!' Susan was taken aback. 'Well, I think that sounds rather high-handed of you. Surely you don't imagine we could come to any harm here, do you?'

'There are all sorts of things that could happen,' replied Dominic, beckoning a steward who hovered near by. 'Fetch me a beer,' he said, 'and what will you have?'

Susan shrugged and walked away from him towards a lounger placed invitingly near the pool.

'Nothing, thank you,' she replied, as she went.

'Bring the lady a glass of lime and lemon,' said her host, ignoring her reply, and the steward went quickly away to get the drinks.

Susan had seated herself on the lounger and Dominic followed her and stood looking down at her quizzically.

'You've changed,' he said, at last, after Susan had begun to feel like an insect under the microscope. 'Not only in looks either. You seem more relaxed, more sure of yourself. Why is that, I wonder?'

Susan looked up at him, refusing to allow the churning of her stomach to interfere with her assumedly unaffected manner.

'Perhaps your son has helped me shed a few of my worries,' she said, and smiled a little. 'Down here, nothing seems as important as it did in London. Who could help but feel the stresses and strains lifting?'

'Very good. I'm glad to hear it,' Dominic smiled in return.

'Where is Jon, anyway?'

'Never mind that; how is Amanda?'

'Well, she seems to be improving rapidly,' said Susan, defensively.

'Strange. I rang the clinic earlier on and I was told she was as yet not responding to treatment.'

Susan compressed her lips for a moment. 'Are you trying to trick me?' she asked, feeling annoyed.

'No. But don't try to whitewash the truth in the hope that I'll go away. I shall leave here when Amanda is back to normal, and not before. I feel like a break, and as I've brought Henry, my secretary, with me, I shall be able to combine business with pleasure, shan't I?'

'Of course, if you say so,' said Susan stiffly.

The steward arrived with the drinks and Susan accepted hers with ill grace. She felt thoroughly out of sorts with everything. Now that Dominic had arrived all her new-found confidence would evaporate.

Dominic drank some of his beer, and then said, 'I think I'll go have a shower. I could do with one.'

'What about Jon? Where is he?'

'Don't worry about Jon. Henry has taken him into Monte Carlo in the car. We drove from Paris,' he said, by way of explanation.

'I see,' Susan nodded.

'And now, excuse me,' he said mockingly, 'and I'll go and remove the dust of travel from my body. I waited to greet you to explain what was going on, but I think I can now go and change, don't you?'

'By all means.' Susan was indifferent and, smiling slightly, Dominic walked away towards the steps leading down to the cabins.

Susan stayed where she was and drank a little of the lime and lemon. It was delicious, the fruits being fresh and squeezed right here on the yacht to make the flavour pure and refreshing. Several squares of ice had been added and they clinked invitingly in the bottom of the glass.

She wondered what Amanda would say when she learned that Dominic had arrived. It was possible whoever spoke to Dominic at the clinic would advise her of his inquiry and Amanda being Amanda would put two and two together and make five.

Finishing her drink she rose and walked slowly down to her cabin. It was nearing the time they usually changed for dinner and she supposed she would have to make an effort and be polite.

The thought occurred to her that should Amanda have to remain in the clinic for any length of time, with Dominic right here to look after Jon himself, her presence became superfluous. She had better consider going back to London sooner than she expected, unless Amanda made a speedy recovery.

The prospect of returning to London was not inviting. Once there, the whole problem of David would emerge again, and she was no farther forward as regards her feelings for him than before.

She dressed after taking a cooling shower, and put on the oyster silk dress she had worn that evening at Fontainebleau. Deciding to attempt to look at least a little sophisticated, she swept her hair up into a French knot and fastened it securely on the crown of her head. The style suited her and made her look older and she felt quite pleased.

Satisfying herself that she was as well turned out as she could achieve, she made her way along to the small, intimate dining saloon where she and Jon and Amanda had been taking their meals. Adjoining this small dining-room there was a much larger one which was used when there were several guests, and afterwards the tables could be folded away and the polished floor used for dancing.

However, the small dining-room was again in use and four places had been laid. Susan presumed the other two were for Jon and Dominic's secretary, Henry.

The room was deserted when she entered and feeling rather uncomfortable she was about to leave and go up on deck when Jon came in.

'Hello, Susan!' he cried gaily. 'Here we are again! How are you, and how was dear Amanda?'

'I'm fine, and Amanda is improving, I think. Did you have a good afternoon?'

'H'm, marvellous. Henry took me for a drive in the new car. It's a Citroën Estate and it's terrific!'

Susan raised her eyebrows at his boyish enthusiasm and when the steward arrived she took a glass of sherry, feeling grateful for the diversion.

'Have you seen Dad, then?'

'Oh, yes, I've seen him.' Susan sipped her sherry.

'You don't sound very pleased. I don't see why not. He's not going to send me back to school, as you thought. He's going to stay on here until Amanda is better. Isn't it wonderful?'

Susan looked a trifle bored. 'If you say so, Jon.'

Jon grimaced. 'Gosh, you're the first woman I've ever met who didn't fall over herself to be friendly towards my father, do you know that?'

Susan smiled. 'Well, perhaps it's because he considers himself just a little bit too knowledgeable about women, and besides, to me, he's usually quite insufferable.'

'Is that a fact?'

Susan swung round, her embarrassment evident for all to see. Dominic Halstad was leaning against the door-post, watching them with cynical amusement in his eyes, and she wondered, in horror, how long he had been standing there.

'Eavesdroppers rarely hear good of themselves,' she said, feeling completely shattered and trying not to show it.

'No, they don't at that. In future I'll let you know when I'm coming and then you can say something nice for me to overhear.'

Susan gave a tight smile. 'I think you're mocking me,' she said, with as much dignity as she could muster, and Jon burst out laughing.

'Oh, Susan, your face! Don't worry, Dad doesn't mind what you say, do you?' He turned to his father:

'Within reason,' remarked Dominic dryly, straightening and walking into the room. 'I see I shall have to be very charming to your playmate, Jon, and then perhaps she'll treat me with the same easy indifference as she treats you.'

Susan felt this remark was rather ambiguous, but refrained from saying so, and felt that the evening had begun extremely badly and would probably end that way.

Dinner was served as soon as Henry Woodward arrived. He was a man in his early sixties, who looked considerably younger. An American, he had worked for Dominic for twenty years in one capacity and another, and was now his personal secretary and friend.

Susan found him quite a charming man, and he treated her gently and undemandingly, which was a blessed relief after mentally crossing swords with Dominic Halstad.

The conversation during the meal centred around Jon and his school work. To Susan's surprise, for she had thought Dominic did not concern himself greatly with Jon's education, he was remarkably well informed about Jon's abilities, and she gathered from their conversation that one day Jon hoped to succeed his father as chairman of the board of Halstad Press.

When the meal was over Dominic rose and said, 'I don't think we'll bore Susan any longer with discussions about business. Tell me,' his eyes were suddenly on her, 'have you been to the Casino yet?'

Susan fingered her wineglass nervously. 'No. Why?'

'Well, I think it's necessary that everyone should visit the Casino at least once while they're in Monte Carlo, don't you agree, Henry?'

Henry grinned. 'Providing, of course, one has the money to do so,' he replied suavely.

'How very diplomatic,' said Dominic, rather sardonically. 'However, as Susan has not been yet, and could hardly go in the company of Amanda alone, I suggest I escort her this evening, while you and Jon spend the evening here in whatever manner suits you best.'

Susan stared at him. 'You haven't asked me whether I would like to go yet,' she said rather bravely.

Dominic raised his dark brows. 'That I haven't! Then would you like to come?'

Susan smiled, and gave in. 'I'd love to,' she agreed.

'Good,' Dominic nodded. 'Very well, shall we go, then?'

The Citröen was, as Jon had said, marvellous. She had never driven with any man except David, and Dominic's style of driving was much different from his. Although he was a much faster driver than David he did not take unnecessary risks and Susan felt safe and secure as his passenger.

As they drove along the coast road, Dominic glanced rather mockingly at his passenger.

'I must admit I think you're being very adventurous, agreeing to come out alone with me like this,' he said lazily.

Susan allowed herself to smile and replied:

'Why? I thought we had managed to sort all that out the last time we met at the apartment.'

Dominic shrugged his broad shoulders, and Susan glancing at him wondered why short hair suited some men and others, like Dominic, looked just as attractive with it needing cutting. At least – she smiled again – she liked it like that. It was such thick hair that she felt an uncontrollable longing to run her fingers through it.

She felt a thrill of apprehension when she realized that they would be spending the rest of the evening alone together. She found herself wondering what she would do if he should touch her, or kiss her. Would she feel as terrified by the action as she did at the thought? After all, he was such an unknown quantity, and the difference in their years was accentuated by their vastly different kinds of lives. If she were one of his own set she would know how to handle him without any difficulty. She would be smooth and sophisticated, and be able to adopt that slightly indifferent air of hauteur affected by fashion models.

'What are you thinking about?'

His words roused her from her reverie and she started in confusion.

'Er – nothing in particular.' She studied the road ahead. 'Will we soon be there?'

'Don't you know? I'm sure you must have been into Monte since you arrived. Anyway, you were there this afternoon.'

'I – I was merely making conversation,' she retorted, and he gave a derisive chuckle.

'Where would you like to have a drink? At the Casino? Or would you like to see a little club I know?'

Susan linked her fingers. 'Anything you say, Mr. Halstad.'

'Dominic,' he said. 'Please.'

'All right, Dominic.' She smiled, and he said:

'Well, I think we'll go to Raphael's.'

Susan inclined her head in agreement, and they turned off the main road and climbed a steep bank into the hills above the harbour.

Raphael's was not, as Susan had vaguely imagined, an ornate night spot, with lots of neon lighting and plushy entrances guarded by commissionaires in liveried uniform. Instead there was a small, dimly lit sign which indicated a flight of steps leading down to a cellar.

Dominic preceded Susan down the steps so that he could help her to negotiate their awkward angles and she was glad when they reached the bottom. Although her heels were not very high she had visions of twisting her ankle and having to limp into the club on one foot.

Dominic looked down at her feet as she reached his side at the foot of the steps and said:

'Are you still in one piece?'

She giggled. 'Just about, I think!'

Dominic's eyes narrowed. 'Do you realize this is the first time you've ever been completely relaxed with me?'

Susan bit her lip. 'Is it? Perhaps it's because I don't feel I have to be on my guard with you at the moment.'

Dominic's fingers curved round the soft flesh of her upper arm.

'Susan,' he murmured softly, and she looked up at him. 'I wish I were years younger, in age and experience.'

'Does it matter?' Susan's voice was husky.

Dominic's fingers hurt her arm. 'Yes, it matters.'

Suddenly the door of the cellar opened and light streamed out on to them. A small, fat, continental man stood, almost filling the doorway, a cigar between his lips, over which a curling moustache curved down to a small beard. His bright almost beady eyes surveyed them for a moment and then he said exuberantly:

'Dominic, *c'est vous?*'

Dominic released Susan and walked fully into the light. 'Yes, Raphael, it's me.'

The man wrung Dominic's hand enthusiastically, and for a moment they spoke in swift French which was completely incomprehensible to Susan.

Then Dominic remembered his companion and drew Susan forward, his arm about her shoulders, casually.

'Susan,' he said, 'I want you to meet Raphael Ortega. With a name like that he ought to be a Spaniard, but he was born here in Monte Carlo, and he's never been any farther than Marseilles all his life, I think.' He grinned. 'Raphael, this is Susan Stacey. She's Amanda Blake's secretary. You remember A.B., don't you?'

'*Oui*, the writer.' Raphael spoke now in English although his accent was very pronounced. 'She is very pretty, my friend. And what would such a pretty girl be doing with you?'

Dominic's grin widened. 'Don't take any notice of him, Susan. He's rather an old roué, I'm afraid.'

Raphael chuckled, and drew them inside, into a wide lobby, discreetly lit, which widened out into a dance floor and bar.

Susan looked round her with interest. The place was not at all imposing, but there was an atmosphere about it of good food and wines, and she felt sure that to enter here required more than the gaudy night clubs favoured by some of the playboy class.

'You like?' asked Raphael, and Susan realized he was speaking to her.

'It's not at all what I expected,' she admitted truthfully, and Dominic nodded.

'I know,' he said, thrusting one hand into the pocket of his trousers. 'You always expect the worst of me for some reason. Did you think I would bring you to a strip club, perhaps? A nude cabaret? Do you think that sort of thing interests me?'

Susan felt embarrassed, feeling deeply conscious of being the cynosure of both Dominic's and Raphael's eyes.

Raphael seemed to take pity on her for he said, 'Don't say things like that to her, Dom. She doesn't know how to answer you.' He chuckled. 'My dear, Dominic is not the kind of man who needs to stimulate himself with that kind of thing.' He looked wryly at his friend. 'Not at all, I would say.'

Susan knew what he meant, and said, at last, 'I know. I'm afraid I always say the wrong thing.'

Dominic raised his dark eyebrows. 'Come on, let's get a drink. I could use one.'

Raphael led the way into the long room which served as dance hall as well as bar. 'You will stay for the cabaret?' he asked Dominic.

Dominic frowned. 'I'm not sure. We're going to the

Casino later. I don't know that we have time. I'm sure Susan expects to be home at a reasonable hour.'

'Reasonable?' Raphael was astounded. 'But what is that?'

Susan stiffened her shoulders. 'I don't expect to be home so early,' she replied. 'Two o'clock would be fine.'

Dominic grinned, albeit a little compassionately. 'All right, honey. That sounds fine.'

Raphael stared at him. 'You are not serious, my friend?'

Dominic shrugged, and Susan sighed. 'Well, what is usual?' she asked exasperatedly.

'To Raphael, first light,' replied Dominic smoothly. 'But I don't keep those hours.'

Susan compressed her lips for a moment. 'Don't expect me to believe that!' she exclaimed.

Dominic seated her by the bar and Raphael went behind to serve them himself, while Susan took the opportunity to survey the room.

It was quite full and a number of couples were dancing to the five-piece group in the corner. Tables were set around the floor, and white-coated attendants were serving a variety of foods. The bar was long and low and modern, lit from end to end with different coloured lights which were the only illumination when the dance floor was in use. There was the glitter of diamonds on throats and wrists and ears, and the aromatic scent of Havana cigars mingling with the unmistakable smell of continental cuisine.

Dominic drew out his cigarette-case and offered Susan one which she took gratefully. She was glad to have something to do to occupy her hands.

He lit himself a cigar and smiled at her through the cloud of blue-grey smoke.

'Do you like it?'

'Hmm, enormously. And I am enjoying myself, even if you do like to bait me.'

Raphael reappeared with two drinks before Dominic could reply, and said:

'My specials! Raphael's.'

Susan gave Dominic a questioning glance, and then sipped her drink tentatively. It was delicious, but very potent, and she gasped a little as the alcohol caught the back of her throat.

Raphael stared at her. 'You like?'

'Yes, I think so. What on earth is in it?'

Raphael shook his head. 'Ah, that is my secret.'

Dominic drank some of his. 'I imagine a couple of these would be sufficient to knock you out,' he said, laughingly, to Susan.

Susan made a face at him and took another sip, forcing herself not to react to the sting at the back of her throat.

Raphael moved away to serve another customer, and Dominic drew deeply on his cigar and said:

'Now, tell me all about yourself.'

Susan shrugged. 'Like what? There's very little to be told.'

'Well, I know that you were brought up in an orphanage; A.B. told me that, and of course I know your fiancé.'

'I think that's all, then. But I'm not sure that David is my fiancé any longer.'

'Why?' Dominic's eyes darkened. 'Did you break it off?'

'It's a long story.' Susan sighed. 'You don't really want to hear about it, do you?'

'Yes, come on.'

'Oh, well, David is dominated by his mother, and she wants us to live with her after we're married, and I have no intention of doing that. You see, we don't get along awfully well.'

'Is that all? I thought you loved him. If you love a person you should be prepared to stand by them, whatever happens.'

'How very old-fashioned of you!'

Dominic half-smiled. 'You think so? Yes, I suppose it is. Actually, I doubt whether I believe it myself. It's simply that that is what you want me to say, isn't it?'

Susan looked thoughtful. 'Well, you see, I met you and suddenly I realized that I had met very few men in my life, and, because I wanted a home of my own, I think I allowed myself to believe I was in love with David. Is that very complicated?'

'Yes, I know what you mean. But don't be blinded, Susan. I think you're being absorbed into this kind of life, Amanda's for example, and knowing Amanda, and how fond she is of you, she's likely to make marriage with any man sound less exciting than continuing to be her secretary.'

'That's very astute of you,' said Susan, smiling. 'Actually, she has already suggested we go to Nassau later in the year, should I not marry David, of course.'

'And what have you decided?'

'Oh, I wrote to David, and asked him to come out here this weekend. When Amanda thought he was coming, she slipped purposefully in order to prevent me going to meet him, hoping she would sprain her ankle or something and be confined to her bed. But it misfired and now she really is ill.'

'The devil she is!' Dominic shook his head. 'And when she discovers that I'm here she'll probably have a blue fit!'

Susan laughed. 'Very probably. But really, she only acts for the best motives, I'm sure. As you say, she is fond of me, and she's the nearest thing to a mother I'm ever likely to have.'

Dominic nodded, and studied his drink. For a moment,

Susan allowed herself the exquisite pleasure of just looking at him. In profile he was no less attractive, and she thought she would never be interested in younger men again. Compared to Dominic, the young men of her acquaintance seemed callow and inexperienced. However hard she might try to dislike him because of his charm for women, she could not succeed. She didn't particularly care about the kind of life he had led, the women he had had. It was now that mattered, and just now he was the most important man in her life. It was a terrible thought, but it could not be denied, regardless of the fact that he was married and apparently had no intention of being otherwise.

Suddenly Susan heard the rustle of an evening gown brush past her, and a gloved hand was laid possessively on Dominic's arm. She saw a tall slim woman standing beside them with thick glossy auburn hair, which hung in rich waves round her shoulders. She was dressed in a gown of silver lamé which clung to her figure like a second skin, accentuating every curve like a loving caress. She looked about twenty-five, although she could possibly be older.

She disregarded Susan completely, and said, 'Darling, I didn't know you were down here!'

Dominic's eyes were lazily undisturbed, and his mouth was curved rather sardonically as he replied:

'Carol. How are you?'

'Darling, what a welcome!' The woman moved closer to him. 'It's wonderful to see you again.'

Susan turned to her drink and tried to stop feeling something like a knife raking about in her stomach. It was pure jealousy and she knew it, and she wondered who on earth this woman was, and what was her relationship to Dominic. It seemed obvious that at some time it had been something more than just a friend.

Dominic had risen to his feet, and the woman called

Carol said, 'Aren't you going to ask me to dance? I have to perform in a little while and I don't get much time between shows.'

Susan looked up then, and met Dominic's eyes. His seemed to be slightly amused, and she quickly looked away again. She wanted to curl up and disappear. She felt grossly *de trop*, particularly as the woman seemed to be openly defying her to speak or do anything.

However, Dominic drew Susan from her seat and said, 'Allow me to introduce our host's charming cabaret artiste, Miss Carol Devereux. Carol, this is Miss Susan Stacey.'

The manner of introduction was not lost on Carol Devereux, but she turned a smiling countenance on Susan, although something like acute dislike burned in her eyes. And Susan realized that she was only being polite because Dominic was there.

After the introduction, Carol Devereux again turned her back on Susan and said:

'Are you staying on the yacht, Dom?'

'Yes. I have Jon with me.'

'Oh!' Carol sounded disappointed, and Susan wondered whether she had ever been a guest aboard the *Ondine*.

'You're staying for the cabaret, of course,' she said, continuing to ignore Susan, and firmly Dominic manoeuvred himself between the two women so that Susan was not simply a bystander.

'I'm not sure. Are we staying, Susan?'

He was deliberately giving her the choice, and Susan, although she wanted with all her heart to leave, heard herself saying, 'I suppose we can. I'd like to see Miss Devereux perform. Just what do you do, Miss Devereux?'

Carol Devereux looked positively taken aback. 'Why, I sing, of course. Do you mean to say you've never heard of me?'

'I'm afraid I haven't.' Susan's voice was cool and detached. 'How long do we have to wait, Dominic?'

Dominic glanced at the gold watch on his wrist. 'About ten minutes. Isn't that right, Carol?'

'You should know, darling. You've heard me often enough,' returned Carol, triumphantly glancing at Susan. 'Now, let's dance; it's been so long.'

Dominic sighed. He looked at Susan as though he thought she might say something, but all she said was, 'Don't mind me!' and sipped stolidly at her drink.

Shrugging, he allowed Carol to draw him out on to the dance floor and Susan refused to look. She did not want to see that woman in Dominic's arms, to see her deliberately provocative, tempting him with words and actions. In all honesty, without being rude, he could hardly have refused, but Susan refused to think that way. Instead, she finished the liquid remaining in her glass and asked Raphael for another.

Raphael looked a little askance, and said, 'Are you sure, Susan?'

'Of course I'm sure. Just give me another, please. I can pay for it.'

'Don't be silly,' said Raphael severely. 'I do not want your money. But these are strong drinks . . . perhaps a little tomato juice, *chérie*?'

Susan shook her head, and Raphael was forced to provide her with another of his 'specials'. However, he did make it a little weaker, even though Susan watched him all the while he was making it to see he did not dupe her.

She lit another cigarette that she accepted from Raphael, and he said:

'This artiste of mine, she has spoiled your evening, yes?'

Susan smiled. 'No. Why should she?'

'Because you think Dominic prefers her to you,' said Raphael bluntly.

'And doesn't he?'

Raphael looked scornful. 'Not at all. This Carol Devereux, she is nothing to him. But women like Dominic; why is obvious, I think.'

Susan drank some of the fiery liquid and studied her glass thoughtfully.

'Is she an old friend of his?'

'An old acquaintance, yes. Years ago, when his wife and her ... well ... associates, came here, Carol was amongst them. She sang one evening with the band, just for fun, I think, and afterwards, when she needed some money she asked me whether I would take her on. I agreed, of course. She is good. But it was not until later that she met Dominic and discovered Veronica was his wife.'

'I gather she's not married, or anything.'

'Divorced now. She was married when she came here with Veronica.'

'I see.' Susan swallowed hard. She was gossiping, and it was unforgivable. Surely it must be the alcohol that was loosening her tongue. She pushed the drink to one side, and smoked her cigarette instead.

The lights on the dance floor had been dipped, but now brightened again, and she glanced round as the music stopped. She saw Carol Devereux and Dominic coming towards her, and with them were two other couples, all talking and laughing together.

She swung round, and hunched her shoulders. Her up-swept hairstyle and attractive dress were not proof against the kind of society women to be found in the clubs of Monte Carlo.

'Here she is!' said Carol Devereux's voice lightly. 'Dominic darling, give me a cigarette. I'm simply dying for a smoke!'

Susan straightened her back, and a slim dark man seated himself beside her.

'Hello again, Miss Stacey.'

Susan looked up sharply. 'Why, Doctor Gervaise,' she exclaimed in surprise.

'Call me Richard. And may I call you Susan?'

Susan was so relieved to see a familiar face she smiled in willing assent.

'Of course,' she said easily. 'How is Miss Blake this evening?'

'She's fine, and please, no more work! I want to forget the clinic for a few hours.' He raised his eyes heavenward.

Susan chuckled. 'And those women?' she asked teasingly.

'Particularly those women,' he agreed, and they laughed together.

'Well, well,' said Carol. 'You two seem to be the best of friends. Poor Angela is quite left out.'

Richard Gervaise gave an apologetic smile to Susan, and then rose to his feet and turned to the rather voluptuous brunette who was standing near by.

Susan rose also, and Carol took over the introductions herself. Susan found that the brunette with Richard was Angela Marriot, daughter of a millionaire banker, and the others were a married couple who were at present on holiday here.

Dominic mercly leaned against the bar, not taking any part in the conversation, and Susan wondered what he really thought about it all. He hardly looked at her although, when Richard began talking to her again, he looked a trifle bored by the whole affair.

'Look,' said Carol, glancing at her watch, 'I have to go now, and sing for the customers, but afterwards I'll ask Raphael if I can miss the midnight cabaret and we could all go to the Casino together. What do you say, Richard?'

Richard looked at Susan, his eyes caressing. 'I think that's a wonderful idea,' he said willingly.

'I'm afraid Susan and I aren't staying for the cabaret, after all,' said Dominic suddenly, stretching his shoulders beneath the immaculate smoothness of his tuxedo.

Susan's eyes widened, but she did not contradict him.

'Oh, but darling . . .' Carol's voice was pleading, 'you promised.'

'I don't recall doing any such thing,' said Dominic easily, his eyes mocking. 'You'll excuse us?'

Richard Gervaise looked disappointed. 'Now, come on, Dominic.'

'Sorry, Rick. See you tomorrow, I guess. I'll be along to see A.B.'

'All right.' Richard gave a helpless shrug and Susan felt Dominic behind her, gently propelling her forward.

She said a swift 'Good-bye' and then preceded him from the club. Raphael was busy with customers and merely waved as they left and in no time at all they were at the top of the steps and crossing to where the Citroën was parked.

Inside the car was darkness and intimacy of a kind that Susan had not experienced on the way out that evening. But now the atmosphere was electric and she felt her whole body tensed and expectant.

Dominic put the keys in the ignition, but he did not switch on. Instead he said:

'The view from here is magnificent, don't you think?'

The whole of Monte Carlo was spread out below them, a mass of twinkling lights.

'Yes.' Susan was abrupt. 'What time is it?'

'A little after eleven; do you want to go back?'

Susan stared at him, unable to read his expression in the darkness.

'No, of course not. It's much too early. Why didn't you agree to go to the Casino with the others?'

'Because I didn't want to go with the others. If I had

wanted to go out in a party, I would have arranged to do just that.' Dominic's voice was curt. 'However, if you're keen, I'm quite willing to return you to the arms of Richard Gervaise, and I'll go back to the yacht now.'

'Dominic!' Susan stared at him, wishing she could see his face. He sounded furious, and she had never known him like this. Even that night in the château at Etoiles he had not been as angry as this.

Dominic turned towards her, his arm along the back of the seat.

'Do you think I'm being cruel?' he asked, 'speaking to you like that? Do you think you can act as you like without it reacting on me in any way whatsoever?'

'What do you mean?'

'I mean that you know absolutely nothing about Richard Gervaise, and yet the minute he speaks to you you're laughing and joking with him as though you'd known him half a lifetime. Me you know everything about, and yet you're continually on your guard, deliberately tormenting me.'

'Dominic!' Susan pressed a hand to her heaving stomach.

'Is that all you can say? Dominic, Dominic?' He ran a hand over his hair restlessly.

'I only know that Richard Gervaise is a bachelor, and you're married,' she replied quietly.

'Married! Married! Do you call the kind of existence I've had over the last ten years marriage?'

Dominic groaned and lay back in his seat as though exhausted. Susan ran a tongue over her lips. She felt she was no longer the same girl who had come out this evening so lightheartedly. Now she was involved, whether she liked it or not, with this man's problems.

'No,' she murmured at last, 'I don't call that marriage.'

'But you still consider me a no-good,' he said harshly. 'And nice girls don't associate with no-goods, do they?'

'Don't be silly. You're no such thing.' Susan moved along the seat until her thigh was touching his. 'You're a very attractive man, and I don't just mean physically.' She studied his face for a moment and then with great daring cupped his face in her hands and kissed his cheek.

'Susan!' he muttered. 'Don't. Please. Don't make me hate myself.'

'Don't you want to kiss me?' She was provocative and appealing. She ran her fingers through his hair, lifting it, loving the feeling of its strength between her fingers.

'Susan,' he groaned, 'I'm only human,' and he pulled her hard against him, his fingers biting into the soft flesh of her shoulders. 'We ought to be elsewhere than in a car,' he murmured, 'but – oh God, I want you!'

His mouth moved over hers exploringly. Susan's bones turned to water. All she was conscious of was the nearness and warmth of this man sweeping her down into an oblivion of feeling where nothing mattered but that this feeling of need should be satisfied by complete surrender.

Until this moment, she realized, she had never known what it was like to be really kissed. Dominic's hard fingers pushed the oyster silk from her shoulders and his mouth found the creamy softness of her throat.

'I adore you,' he murmured, his mouth moving over her neck searchingly, and back to her mouth again. 'Adore you. Kiss me – Susan—'

Susan then knew what Amanda had meant when she had warned her about Dominic. She was completely incapable of resisting him and she knew that had he wanted to make love to her there and then she would have let him.

But at last Dominic gently pushed her away from him, and said:

'Honey, you have no idea what you're doing to me.'

He reached into his pocket and drew out his cigarettes and after lighting two he handed her one.

Susan took the cigarette and tried to calm her pounding heart. This was no good. She must have been crazy. It must have been the drinks she had consumed. How had she dared to lead him on like that? What must he think of her?

Dominic studied her for a moment and then he began to take the hairpins out of her hair, causing it to fall loosely about her shoulders.

'Don't put your hair up. I don't like it,' he murmured softly.

Susan ran a shaky hand over her hair. 'I expect it looks an awful mess now,' she said nervously.

'No, it doesn't,' he said softly. 'It looks delicious, even in this murky light.'

Susan shivered suddenly.

'Are you cold?'

'No.' Susan shook her head. 'What time is it?'

Dominic sighed. 'Are you obsessed with the time? What does it matter? If you must know, it's nearly twelve.'

'Oh!' Susan drew on her cigarette, and with a sigh Dominic threw his cigarette out of the window and pulled her back into his arms.

'Now what's wrong? Are you sorry I touched you?'

Susan felt her whole body tingling as she leaned against him. 'I . . . I shouldn't have done . . . what I did.'

'Why not? Do you think I didn't want to touch you?'

'And did you?' Susan looked up at him.

'Oh, darling,' he groaned, his mouth caressing her neck. 'You must know I want you, and it's hell knowing that I can't have you.'

He turned her face up to his, smoothing back the hair from her forehead with his thumbs. His fingers tangled themselves in her silky hair and he said:

'Do you remember the first time I saw you at the

apartment when you were so annoyed because I didn't do as you wanted?'

Susan smiled. 'Yes, I remember. Why?'

'Well, I knew then that you and I were not meant to be indifferent to one another.' He kissed her eyelids gently. 'I wanted to ask you to see me again even then, but Amanda told me you were engaged and that was that.'

'But why? I'm so ordinary.'

He caressed her shoulders, awakening her senses fully to his ardour.

'Ordinary!' he murmured. 'I guess you might say that, but not to me. Your eyes are anything but ordinary, and there's a certain something about you that attracts me more than mere beauty.' His mouth sought hers again, and at last he was forced to push her away. 'We'd better go back,' he said harshly. 'I'm in no mood for the Casino tonight.'

'But, Dominic—' Susan felt suddenly depressed, 'if we go back the evening will be over.'

'Yes. Over.' Dominic's face had assumed its rather mocking expression.

He swung the car round and drove back down the road, turning towards Delice when they reached the main thoroughfare. Susan shivered. For a moment things had been different, but now they were back to normal again. And it was obvious that Dominic had no intention of breaking faith with Amanda by seducing her secretary.

She felt like crying. It was what she wanted, of course, and yet she wished secretly that he had taken advantage of her. She scoffed at herself. What price now her statement that she could handle Dominic? How foolish she must have seemed to Amanda who knew Dominic so much better than she did.

And yet did she?

Amanda had never known the side of Dominic that

Susan now knew and cherished. The gentle, persuasive lover who could make a girl forget everything but a longing to satisfy him and become completely herself in their union.

CHAPTER TEN

THE Manning Clinic stood in its own grounds near Central Park in New York. It was a newly built building with lots of wide windows and patios, where the patients could sit in the sun and enjoy the strengthening rays as the spring turned into summer.

It wa run by Philip Manning, a man in his late forties, who had specialized in psychology and psychiatric work before opening the clinic. His patients were in the main wealthy men and women who had temporarily gone off the rails for some reason or another and were now in the course of being rehabilitated. Many of his cases were of a more serious nature than Veronica's, and Dominic knew that she kept herself very much apart from any unpleasantness.

For a time she had been interested in Manning himself, but he was a married man and had made it clear that he was not interested. He had even mentioned it to Dominic, who had felt embarrassed and somehow responsible for Veronica's irresponsible behaviour.

Dominic, who had landed in New York only a few hours earlier, had driven to the clinic and was now waiting to see Philip Manning. He had to see Manning first to see how Veronica was progressing and then he was going to see his wife and ask her for a divorce.

Although it was only two o'clock in the afternoon, Dominic felt he needed a drink, and paced about the waiting-room restlessly, wanting to get this interview over as quickly as possible.

He lit a cigar and drew on it deeply, wondering what Susan would say when he flew back and told her he had asked Veronica for a divorce.

The door opened and a Sister appeared. 'Will you come this way?' she said, smiling and holding the door open for him to follow her.

Stubbing out his cigar, Dominic loosened his overcoat and did as he was bidden, following the woman across the marble tiled entrance hall and into an outer office at the other side of the hall. 'Mr. Manning will see you now,' she said, indicating the door leading to the inner office which was Manning's own sanctum where much of his theoretical work was accomplished.

'Thank you,' Dominic nodded, and knocking on the door he entered Philip Manning's office. Manning was standing by the window as he entered, and turned to smile at his visitor.

'Hello, Dominic. How are you?'

'I'm fine, thanks.' Dominic shook hands, and then they both seated themselves in the armchairs on opposite sides of the desk.

'Cigarette?' asked Manning, indicating the box on the desk, and Dominic nodded and took one, lighting it swiftly from his platinum lighter.

'Now,' he said, 'how is she?'

Manning lay back in his seat, the tips of his fingers together.

'Well,' he began, 'to be quite honest, if you hadn't arrived today so unexpectedly, I was going to get in touch with you again. The suicidal tendencies we spoke of earlier have become manifest.'

'What!' Dominic studied the man opposite him. 'But when I saw you earlier, you gave me to understand that they were simply part of her illness and that once the depression was lifted she would begin to be normal again. The drugs were supposed . . .' He halted. 'All right, Philip, go on.'

Philip Manning looked disturbed. 'Veronica is in a very depressed state at the moment. When I spoke to you before I thought it was a temporary relapse. She'd been definitely improving. Unfortunately, I think all this stems from Arnold Harrison.'

Dominic sighed, and lay back wearily. 'Why? Has he ditched her again?'

'I'm afraid so. Dominic, don't look like that! Man, it's not your affair.'

'But it is.' Dominic flicked the ash off his cigarette into a brass ashtray on the desk. 'I was going to ask her for a divorce today.'

Manning stared at him. 'A divorce! I see.' He looked nonplussed. 'This is sudden, isn't it? You never said anything about a divorce the last time we spoke together.'

'I know.' Dominic shrugged. 'Sometimes these things happen like that.'

'You want to marry someone else, I take it?'

'Yes. Not that it's any affair of yours,' muttered Dominic moodily. 'Even if you are Veronica's doctor.'

'I know. It's simply that I don't think now is a good time to ask her. A month, two months ago, I would have said she would probably have welcomed it. She's not a young woman any longer, and I really think she wants to marry this Harrison man. Unfortunately, he doesn't feel the same.'

'He's a hanger-on,' muttered Dominic angrily. 'He only wants her for her money.'

'I should think in the state she's in at present, no man would want her for any other reason,' replied Manning bluntly. 'Oh, Dominic, what can I say? Why on earth didn't you divorce her years ago? In the beginning.'

'Because I felt sorry for her,' said Dominic heavily.

'And besides, I never believed I would ever want to marry anyone else.'

'I see.' Manning sighed. 'So where do we go from here?'

'Tell me about her, Philip. What's happened to cause you to need to contact me?'

'She tried to drown herself in the bath.'

'But that's impossible!'

'No, it's not impossible. Not if you've just taken a strong sleeping draught. We always ascertain that she takes her sleeping tablets when they're given to her, just in case she ever tried to hoard a few in order to poison herself that way. She's had tendencies like this since Harrison left her. And cases of her sort have gotten away with it. The Manning Clinic can do without that kind of publicity.'

'I can believe that.' Dominic sighed heavily. 'All right, I understand you. I'm sorry if I seem jaded, but I wanted to be free of her once and for all. When can I see her?'

'I've sent for her—' Manning's voice halted abruptly, as the door was thrown open. 'Veronica! How long have you been there?'

Dominic sprang to his feet and turned round. Veronica stood where she was, a mocking smile on her face as she surveyed the pair of them.

'Well, well!' she said. 'The guilty parties!'

'I don't understand you,' said Manning, trying to retain his composure. 'Where is Nurse Standish?'

Veronica strolled into the room, closing the door. 'Darling, you sent for me. Standish simply delivered me to your office and expected me to walk straight in. Instead, I practised a little of the old eavesdropping, and, as all eavesdroppers do, I heard ill of myself. So dear old Dominic wants a divorce. How very amusing!'

Dominic and Philip Manning looked as surprised as they felt. Veronica surveyed them sardonically, and laughed. 'Poor Dominic,' she said, 'you seem quite disturbed. It's so difficult to get under your skin, but I think for once I've actually caught you out.'

Dominic tried to regain his composure as Manning had done.

'You always liked to spring surprises on people, Veronica,' he said. 'And usually they were not particularly pleasant ones.'

Veronica shrugged. 'Why are you here? Did you actually come to ask me for a divorce, or did Philip send for you? I expect he did. I can't honestly imagine cold, cynical Dominic being impulsive enough actually to want some woman sufficiently to rush here to get my permission. After all, that's not entirely necessary, in the circumstances, is it?'

Dominic stiffened his shoulders. 'Whatever you've done, Veronica, you're still my wife, if in name only, and I would always do you the courtesy of asking your permission in any matters which connect us personally.'

Philip looked uncomfortable. 'Look,' he said, 'I'll leave you here. I have to see my patients in any case, and I'll return later and you can let me know what's been decided.'

'Why should we?' Veronica stared at him coldly. 'You're my doctor, not my solicitor.'

Philip shrugged at Dominic and left the room. Dominic closed the door after him and Veronica said:

'Everything you do has to be so *proper*!' in a tight voice. 'God, don't you ever relax?'

'Not with you,' said Dominic quietly. 'But let's get down to business. I gather you'll have no objections to the divorce?'

Veronica helped herself to a cigarette before replying, and in the meantime Dominic had an opportunity to study her. Her once red hair was now streaked with grey, but he knew that once she was out of the clinic it would be retinted back to its original colour. Although she was wearing a heavy make-up, the lines on her skin and the unhealthy pallor were only slightly concealed, and Dominic felt a rush of pity. He wondered whether, had he stayed at home more, she would have been any different. It seemed doubtful. She had always been restless and discontented, and positively furious when she had learned she was pregnant.

Veronica turned back to him, wrapping the folds of the emerald-green housecoat she was wearing closely about her. She removed the cigarette from her lips, and surveying him rather mockingly, she said:

'Well now, Dominic, the divorce rather depends on you.'

Dominic frowned. Veronica's thoughtful expression disturbed him intensely. There was about her an air of suppressed elation, and she seemed to be secretly laughing at him for some reason. For a woman who a few days ago had attempted to commit suicide, she seemed strangely excited.

'In what way does it depend on me?' Dominic spread wide his hands. 'Naturally I shall continue to supply you with funds. I shouldn't expect you to have to support yourself at any time—'

'How noble of you!' Veronica seated herself in Philip's chair. 'Unfortunately, that's not all I want.'

'Not all you want?' Dominic was puzzled. 'What do you mean?'

Veronica savoured her words. 'I want Jon,' she said calmly. 'It's as easy as that!'

'You must be mad!' The words sprang from Dominic's mouth involuntarily. He strode across to the desk angrily, leaning on his hands and staring at her incredulously.

'Why? For wanting my son?'

Dominic shook his head. 'But why now? You've never cared about him before.'

'Did you honestly imagine you could come here and be granted a divorce without any conditions?' Veronica laughed. 'Why should I allow you to go and marry some strange girl just because it suits you to do so?'

'But, Veronica, our marriage hasn't been a marriage for years! Lord, I could prove that quite easily.'

'Yes, you could,' she agreed mockingly. 'But you won't, will you? I mean, if I should attempt to defend the suit, just think what would come out! Your petty little world would come tumbling about your ears!'

'It's not my world I'm concerned about,' muttered Dominic. 'It's Jon's. Do you think I want the Halstad name dragged through the mud? Do you think I want Jon to have to suffer the torment of the publicity of his mother being an alcoholic?'

'Well, darling, you have the answer. Let me have Jon. After all, he hardly knows me.'

'No.' Dominic swallowed hard. 'No. I'd rather do anything than let you get your hands on that boy! Knowing full well, too, that you're only taking him to spite me! God, Veronica, I knew you were weak and selfish, but I didn't know you were vindictive, too. You know no court in any civilized country would give you the custody of Jon. That's why you're making it a condition of your consent. But I'm sorry, I can't agree.'

Veronica shrugged. 'Ah, well! That's your affair.'

Dominic clenched his fists, and pulling out his cigarcase he extracted one and put it between his teeth, feeling enraged and impotent. Without Veronica's consent that she would not defend the case he knew he must refuse to take the plunge. He could not allow Jon to be injured in this case. Hadn't they injured him enough already, breaking up his home and forcing him to grow up years before his time? And he knew, also, that he could not permit Veronica to become his guardian again. Jon was at an impressionable age. At the moment, Susan's pleasant, uncomplicated character was working wonders for him, but if he should be plunged again into the quagmire Veronica had made of her life, it might influence him terribly, and to his detriment in later years.

'Look, Veronica,' he said desperately, 'you don't really want Jon. After all, boys of that age require entertainment during the holidays, and besides, when your friends find you have a son of Jon's age, it will age you enormously.' He sighed. 'Look, I'm quite willing to make it worth your while, in addition to your usual allowance, of course. Say a hundred thousand pounds, as a down payment.'

Veronica merely laughed and shook her head. 'I don't want money,' she said, destroying the faint hope that had arisen. 'Don't I know that any money you gave me would be simply a drop in the ocean as far as you're concerned? I know I can't trust you that way, but with Jon, I think I have a chance.' She leaned forward and stubbed out her cigarette. 'But, my God, Dom, I never realized you could want a woman that much! Where did I go wrong, I wonder? Couldn't we start again and find out?'

Dominic looked appalled, as he thought for a moment she was serious, and Veronica's mouth twisted. 'Oh, don't worry, Dominic, I didn't mean it. There's only one man I want, and at the moment he doesn't want me.'

'Arnold Harrison.'

'Precisely. And he'll come back, I – I know he will!' But she did not sound very sure.

Dominic was nauseated by the whole affair and he wanted to get away. His disappointment was like ashes in his mouth and the prospect of never being able to have Susan as his wife was agonizing. He was relieved when a few minutes later Philip returned, and he was able to make his departure. There was nothing more to be said, and nothing he could do.

CHAPTER ELEVEN

Susan lay on the deck of the *Ondine*, dressed only in a one-piece bathing suit of sapphire-blue poplin. She looked young and healthy and tanned, and only her eyes mirrored the painful reactions she was experiencing since Dominic's abrupt departure. Henry Woodward was still on the yacht, apparently left in charge by Dominic, but if he knew where his employer had gone then he was not telling anyone. Even Jon did not know, although he did not seem unduly perturbed and Susan could only assume that he was used to Dominic behaving in this manner, here today and gone tomorrow.

It was two days since Dominic left. He had gone the morning after he arrived, after their fateful night out together. Susan could only imagine that it was for that reason he had left. Perhaps he could not bear to be on the same boat as her, having to face her every day with the knowledge that she was merely a passing whim whereas she obviously had treated it as something more. Had she behaved foolishly? Had she embarrassed him by practically forcing him to touch her? Whatever he had said, she could not move the feeling of guilt she felt, and had felt since that evening.

That first morning she had written to David, though, and told him once and for all that they were through. Whatever happened now she knew she could never go back to David. Not now! Not after knowing what it was like to be loved by Dominic Halstad. She would never be the same girl again.

She jumped, startled, as Jon came to fling himself beside her and said:

'Are you going to see A.B. this afternoon?'

'I expect so. Why? Do you want to come? She was

asking about you yesterday. Asking why you hadn't gone with me. I explained that Henry had taken you to Cannes with him in the Citroën, and that you were in good hands.'

'Well, at least with Dad leaving so suddenly she hasn't had to concern herself with his affairs.' remarked Jon shrewdly. 'I wonder why he only stayed such a short time. After all, he didn't get any urgent messages, because I asked Mac, and with Henry here he can't have gone away on business. He always takes Henry with him when he's attending any conferences.'

'Why don't you ask Henry, then?'

'I have. But he's a past master at the art of evasion. All I get out of him is that Dad will be back and then I'll be able to ask him for myself.'

'Your father is coming back?'

'So Henry says, although if Amanda gets out of the clinic tomorrow as she hopes to do, he won't have anything to stay for, will he?'

'No,' admitted Susan, half regretful and half thankful. At least Amanda's presence would eliminate any *tête-à-têtes* between the two of them.

Jon rolled on to his stomach and glanced at his watch. 'Oh, good, it's nearly lunchtime. I'm starving. What time are you going to see Amanda?'

'About three-thirty. Are you coming?'

'I guess so. But I never know what to say to people when they're in hospital. It always seems such an artificial conversation.'

Susan had to smile. 'Well, so long as you show your face, I don't expect Amanda will mind if you spend the time munching her grapes, and reading her magazines.'

Jon chuckled, 'Okay, you've convinced me. I'll come.'

Lunch was served in the small saloon. Henry joined them. Since staying on the yacht, he had shed his formal manner and mode of dress, and had become a very likeable character. He was dressed today in cream slacks and shirt with a multi-coloured silk scarf slotted cravat-wise at his throat.

Susan had merely donned a white towelling coat over her bathing costume and Jon wore only his trunks. Susan thought they looked very informal and said:

'If anyone could see us now our relationship would certainly arouse some concern.'

Henry grinned. 'I imagine it would. However, as no one is likely to see us the situation doesn't arise.'

Suddenly, the steward who had been serving the shrimp cocktails and who had been out of the saloon for a moment to get the dressing returned, and said:

'Excuse me, but there is a young gentleman asking to come aboard from a launch who says he is a friend of Miss Stacey's.'

Susan almost dropped the glass of wine she had been sipping, and said:

'A friend of mine? Did he give his name?'

'I believe it's a Mr. Chalmers. Chalmers, yes.'

Susan was flabbergasted, and Henry said with concern, 'Susan, what's wrong? Do you know this man?'

'Yes. He used to be my fiancé,' said Susan faintly. 'But I can't imagine why he's come here.' Or was that strictly true?

'Do you want me to deal with him, then?' Henry rose to his feet.

Susan rose also, shaking her head. 'No, no, of course not. I'll see him.'

She walked quickly out of the saloon, and up the companionway to the deck. The steward hurried before her and by the time she emerged on deck feeling very apprehensive, David was standing by the steps which he had climbed from the launch below, and was looking about him with interest.

159

When he saw Susan, he marched briskly across to her and said:

'Is there somewhere we can talk without interruption?' He glanced round at the curious gazes of the crew, who were watching their meeting with avid enthusiasm.

Susan ran a tongue over her dry lips. 'I can't see what we have to say to one another,' she said quietly. 'I wrote everything there was to say in my letter. I'm sorry, David, but if that's why you've come, you've had a wasted journey.'

'Of course it's why I've come,' he snapped, and she realized he was very angry.

Feeling it would be as well for them to be out of the sight of the rest of the crew, Susan said:

'Very well, we'll go to the lounge. There won't be anyone there at this hour of the day.'

'Good. Lead on.'

The lounge was a large comfortable cabin fitted with red leather furniture and an off-white carpet. A cocktail cabinet was fitted cross-wise across one corner and, feeling rather uncomfortable, Susan said, 'Would you like a drink? Something long and cool and refreshing?'

David shrugged. 'If you like. Now, what do you mean by sending me that letter? I was absolutely flabbergasted.'

'But why? Surely you realized before I came away that things couldn't have been worse?'

'You only wrote to me a week ago asking me to come out here,' retorted David.

'I know. That was a stupid thing to do and I'm sorry. But your letter to me proved that you were more concerned with money than with our future happiness. There are times, David, when you can't see the wood for the trees. You simply refuse to accept the obvious. Surely you can see that we're just not compatible.'

'I only know that since meeting Dominic Halstad you've changed from a sensible, home-loving girl into a . . . a . . .' He sought about for a word to describe her. 'Look at you now! That outfit! I mean to say, it's just not the thing!'

'Don't be silly, David. It's too hot to wear fussy clothes out here. Why, even the men wear only trunks and tee-shirts most of the time.' She sighed. 'Anyway, that's nothing to do with anything. What I wear in future will be my concern only.'

'You're going to marry me, Susan.' David sounded very sure of himself. 'And we're going to live with Mother until we can afford to buy a really nice house, not one of those tiny things we've been considering.'

Susan shook her head. 'No, David. I'm sorry, but that will not do. I don't love you, and even if I did I'm not stupid enough to expect you ever to leave Medlar Grove while your mother is alive. I'm only thankful that I found out as I did. If I'd never met Dominic—'

'Dominic! Dominic!' David snorted angrily. 'Is he here now?'

'No. There's only Jon and me and Henry Woodward, Dominic's assistant. Amanda has had an accident and is in a clinic on the mainland. She hopes to be back tomorrow.'

'Indeed.' David caught Susan by the shoulders. 'So we're alone, it seems. I imagine this fellow Woodward wouldn't interrupt us if we chose to spend a little time together.'

Susan moved to the door. 'I think the sun must be affecting your brain,' she said, sounding much calmer than she felt. 'Please go, David. Don't make me call the steward.'

David clenched his fists. 'You wouldn't!' he exclaimed.

'I'm afraid I'd have to,' said Susan. 'Please, David. I'm truly sorry.'

David shrugged. 'And do you expect to marry this man? This *married* man?'

Susan shook her head. 'No, I don't expect to do that,' she replied, rather wistfully. 'I shall remain Amanda's secretary. She's wanting to go to the Bahamas later in the year, so I expect I shall go with her.'

'And what about Delia?'

'Delia is going to marry Alan Huntley. She won't need me, and when I return to England I shall probably find someone else to share the flat.'

She opened the door and walked out, waiting for him to follow her. David followed her slowly, looking angry and petulant. On deck, a breeze lifted Susan's hair, and David's face darkened as he realized what he had lost.

'Won't you reconsider?' he began, but she shook her head, and he beat one fist into the palm of his other hand. 'You'll be sorry,' he said, as a parting shot, and strode across to where his boat was moored.

As he reached the steps he halted, and Susan put a hand to her throat, wondering what now. Then she realized he was waiting for someone to reach the top of the steps before he could descend. She frowned. Who could it be? Surely not Dominic! Her heart turned over.

But it was! Dominic himself, looking incredibly young and attractive as he appeared in a light-grey lounge suit and a white shirt and a dark-grey knitted tie. His eyes narrowed as he saw David, and he said:

'Hello, Chalmers. Here for a visit?'

Susan linked her fingers nervously. What now?

'No.' David was abrupt. 'Are you?'

Dominic glanced at Susan. 'Didn't Susan tell you?'

'I understood from Susan you were not here.' David gave Susan a withering look. 'It seems she was wrong.'

Susan made a helpless gesture, and Dominic merely raised his shoulders slightly and let them fall again.

'Well, don't let me keep you.' Dominic's voice was cool.

'Thank you, I won't. Good-bye, Susan.'

'Good-bye, David.' Susan's voice was a trifle tremulous and Dominic looked sardonic. As the launch bearing David drew away from the yacht and headed back for the shore, Dominic strolled across to Susan.

'Well?' he said questioningly. 'You didn't waste much time. Why did you send for him?'

Susan looked up at him. 'It might interest you to know that I didn't send for him.'

'Then why was he here? I thought he'd refused to come earlier.'

'He had.' Susan turned away. 'Lunch is waiting. I'll tell the steward you've arrived.'

Dominic's fingers gripped her arm. 'No, don't go. I'm not particularly hungry anyway. I want to talk to you.'

Susan sighed. 'Look, Dominic, I'm sorry if I embarrassed you the last time we were together. But I don't want to talk about it any more. It's over.'

Dominic's fingers tightened their grip and bit into her flesh. 'Have you been discussing me with Chalmers?' he ground out, between his teeth.

Susan swung round. 'As if I would! Don't be silly. And you're causing a sensation among your staff. After David's exhibition earlier, I should think they're getting to enjoy it.'

'Why? What did he do?'

Susan pulled herself free of him. 'It's nothing to do with you.'

'Look, Susan,' he muttered, 'I'm determined to know the truth about Chalmers' visit, and the sooner you tell me the better it will be for all concerned.'

'Well, let's go down to the lounge, please. I don't propose to discuss my affairs here.'

'Very well, let's.' Dominic took Susan's arm again and they walked swiftly down the companionway. A feeling like hysteria swept over Susan, as she contemplated what the crew must be thinking of her, and she suppressed it guiltily.

Dominic shut the cabin door and then releasing her he walked across to the cocktail cabinet and helped himself to a lager from the refrigerated cabinet at the back.

'Do you want a drink?' he asked coldly, but Susan shook her head. 'Okay, then, let's have it. Why did he come?'

Susan twisted her fingers together. It was going to be difficult to explain without revealing her feelings for Dominic.

'I wrote to him and told him finally that we were through,' she replied quietly. 'Amanda has made me realize that the real reason I was marrying David was for a home and the security that brings. I now see things differently. Amanda was right about David. He's weak, and I've been weak too, allowing him to think things were the same between us. I'm afraid he allows his mother too much dominance in his affairs. And that's why he came. Because he thought I'd only written that to bring him out here.'

'And so? What was the outcome?'

'I told him I hadn't changed my mind, and he's gone home again. That's all there is to it.'

Dominic swallowed half his drink, and then placed the glass on the glass-topped bar and walked across to where she was standing. Placing his hands on her shoulders, he said, 'And me? Don't I have anything to do with it at all?'

She shivered. All at once she knew she had to tell the truth to this man. He deserved nothing less.

'Yes,' she said, looking up at him. 'You know you have everything to do with it.'

Dominic's arms closed around her, and his mouth sought hers, gentle at first and then hardening with passion. Susan's arms slid round his waist inside his jacket, next to the warmth of his skin which she could feel through the thin silk of his shirt. She pressed herself against him and whispered:

'Oh, Dominic, I love you.'

Dominic pulled her down on to a low couch, still in his arms, and burying his face in the softness of her hair, he muttered:

'I went to ask Veronica for a divorce.'

Susan drew back and looked at him. 'A divorce! Dominic . . . for me?'

Dominic pulled her back to him. 'Yes, for us, Susan. I wanted to marry you. Unfortunately her conditions were unacceptable.'

Susan felt her earlier elation fading. 'Jon,' she murmured matter-of-factly.

Dominic stared at her. 'How did you know?'

Susan shrugged. 'I didn't. I guessed. But I'm a woman, and I can imagine that Jon is the only weapon she could hold over you. But no court would ever allow her the custody of him, would they?'

'Oh, no. But she realizes that. She wants me to let her have Jon in exchange for not defending the case. She knows I won't divorce her without her consent for Jon's sake. I don't want him to suffer the publicity that that would arouse.'

Susan nodded. 'I can see that. And Jon has been hurt enough already.'

'Ah, Susan,' he murmured brokenly, 'if only I were free!'

Susan sighed, and lay back against the red leather upholstery, looking at him seriously. 'How important is being the head of the Halstad Press to you?' she asked suddenly.

Dominic reached for his cigars. 'Importance doesn't come into it. It's my job.'

'But would you give it up?' Susan was staring at him.

Dominic frowned. 'For you? Yes, I guess I'd do anything for you. But I can't see how that would help us.'

'Well,' Susan hesitated for a moment, 'I can quite see that my presence with you in London would cause an awful lot of embarrassment and speculation, especially for Jon, but if we were to go somewhere else, away from the rat-race, it wouldn't matter—'

'If you mean what I think you're meaning,' said Dominic gently, 'the answer is no. Do you think for one moment I would turn you into a kept woman?'

Susan smoothed her hair back, twisting the tendrils behind her ears. His reply proved to her, as nothing else could have done, that he loved her for herself and not just because of her youth and beauty.

'So what now?' Susan felt empty inside. Whatever comfort she might derive from Dominic's love for her, they had reached a point of impasse and there seemed nothing left for them to say.

Dominic shrugged his broad shoulders. 'You continue to be Amanda's secretary and I continue to bury myself in my work. One day . . . who knows? And anyway, you might meet someone else, some time, who is free, and who can offer you much more than I can—'

'Don't, please, Dominic, don't.' Susan buried her face in her hands, the hot tears scalding her fingers. 'Don't even think it! I couldn't marry anyone else. Not now!'

Dominic groaned. 'I'm only trying to think of you, Susan. Do you think the thought of you with some other man doesn't drive me crazy with jealousy? But you're so young. You've your whole life ahead of you, whereas I've already made a mess of mine.'

'You were not to blame.'

'I tell myself that, but I wonder whether another man

might have made Veronica so happy that she wouldn't have gone off the rails as she did.'

Susan shook her head. 'You know that's only a guilt complex,' she said. She rose to her feet. 'I'd better get back to the others. Jon will have finished lunch by now and be looking for me.'

Dominic nodded. 'I'll see you later.' His voice was husky. 'I'll wait until Amanda gets back and then I'll leave. It will be doubtful that we'll ever see each other again. I – I'll try and keep out of Amanda's way, so as not to cause you any embarrassment—'

Susan turned away. 'Oh, Dominic, please!' she begged. 'I want to see you again. Don't avoid me, please!'

Dominic crushed his cigar into an ashtray, and rose too, looking down on her bowed head in exasperation.

'Go on,' he said, 'before I touch you again.' He walked over to the cocktail cabinet. 'I need a drink!'

Susan walked slowly along to the saloon where lunch had been served. It was empty. Not feeling like food any longer, she refused the steward who came to serve her, and leaving the room went along to her own cabin. Once there she flung herself on the bed and allowed the hot tears to flow. Crying eased the nervous system and just now she felt her nerves were shot to pieces. And she had to go and see Amanda later and not appear at all disturbed. How was she going to do it?

Amanda returned to the yacht the following afternoon. Her ankle was still strapped up and her ribs were encased in a plaster cast, but she was cheerful enough to be back again, and full of ideas for a new story. It was to be set in a clinic in the South of France and she admitted the rather over-indulged hypochondriacs at the clinic had given her the ideas.

The weather had changed and it had begun to rain during the morning and overcast skies showed little signs of improvement. Jon was restless; unable to swim or play deck-games with the crew, he followed Susan about like a shadow until she felt like screaming. She was feeling tense and disturbed herself and at last said:

'For goodness' sake, Jon, go and get a book to read and stop trailing after me!'

Jon stared at her in surprise. 'What's wrong with you? You aren't normally like this. Don't you want Amanda to come back?'

'Of course I do.' Susan moved helplessly. 'I'm just fed up, that's all. Just leave me alone.'

Jon snorted, annoyed. 'It seems to me that I'd be far better off with my mother at times like this,' he said surprisingly, and Susan gasped. 'It's true,' he continued. 'My father is acting like a bear with a sore head, and you can't even stand the sight of me.'

'That's not true,' she exclaimed. 'It's nothing to do with you, honestly, Jon. I'm just distraught, that's all.'

'Well, anyway, I'm fed up too. Did you know my father had been to see my mother?'

Susan flushed. 'Well, yes, actually I did. Why?'

'You see! Nobody tells me anything.'

'Then how did you find out?'

'I heard Henry talking to Dad. They were talking about my mother, and I gathered Dad had been to the States to see her. I wonder why, when he'd just arrived here. Do you think she's all right?'

'I think so. But anyway, it's nothing to do with me, is it?'

'No, I guess not. But I wish I knew.'

Susan moved across the lounge where they were talking and idly turned on the stereophonic radiogram. In a few hours Dominic would be leaving and it was almost more than she could bear.

Amanda, once installed in her cabin, sent for Susan, and said:

'You're looking ill. What's wrong with you?'

'Nothing. It must be the change in the weather,' Susan lied. 'How are you feeling?'

'Never mind me, I want to know about you. It's Dominic, isn't it?'

Susan turned her hands palms upwards. 'Why do you ask, if you already know?'

'Because I wanted to be sure. Susan, Susan, what did I tell you?'

'It's not what you think,' said Susan slowly. 'Dominic loves me. He asked Veronica for a divorce, but she refused him.'

Amanda was absolutely astounded and looked it. 'Are you serious?'

'Of course I am. But it doesn't make any difference, does it? Dominic won't have me any other way and so he's leaving tomorrow.'

Amanda shook her head. 'Dear heaven,' she exclaimed. 'I would never have believed it! But I don't understand. Dominic doesn't need Veronica's consent, does he? He has every right to a divorce.'

'Legally, yes, but he won't do it without her consent because of Jon. If she defended there would be a frightful scandal.'

'I see. Of course he's right.' Amanda groaned. 'But how can Veronica act this way after all these years?'

Susan shrugged her shoulders. 'I don't know. But she has, and that's that.' She was trying to sound indifferent, but she failed dismally, and Amanda was compassionate.

'Whatever can I say?' she asked. 'I only wish there was something I could do. What will you do, then? Can I take it that you'll be continuing as my secretary?'

Susan nodded. 'Yes. If you'll have me.'

'Don't talk nonsense! Of course I'll have you. I never

wanted you to marry that Chalmers man, you know that. Jon tells me he came here yesterday.'

'Yes. When I wrote and told him of my final decision, he must have thought it was simply a ruse to get him out here. At any rate, he came, but I told him it was no good.'

'Do you still feel that way, knowing Dominic can't get free?'

'Oh, yes. I'd decided that before I even knew Dominic was serious about me. You see, I realized that I couldn't marry David, or any other man, feeling as I do about Dominic. I don't suppose I shall ever marry, unless in a few years' time Veronica decides to divorce Dominic after all, and then maybe he'll come back for me.' She clasped her hands. 'I'd wait for ever for that to happen!'

Amanda sighed. 'My dear! What can I say?'

'Nothing. There's nothing to be said. Now, what about this new novel? What's it going to be about? Are there lots of gruesome bodies found in the operating theatre?'

Taking her mood from Susan, Amanda changed the subject, and they began to discuss the characters and situations for the new book. But Amanda could see that Susan's heart just wasn't in it and she wished with all her might that Veronica had never married Dominic in the first place.

Dinner that evening was a solemn meal. Both Dominic and Susan were engrossed with their own private despair, and Amanda felt the kind of desperate impotence that any friend might feel at the callousness of fate that had thrown these two together, only to separate them again.

Jon, too, was moody. He had not got over his earlier argument with Susan, and kept casting reproachful glances in her direction, which she was terribly conscious of.

Only Henry Woodward seemed free of depression, and tried his utmost to draw them all into conversation, without a great deal of success. He only knew a little of what had happened, but, astute as he was, he had guessed the rest, and hoped the morning would come swiftly so that the separation might take place and be done with. He knew Veronica, and like Dominic, could not see her changing her mind. By holding on to Jon she was hurting Dominic more than she had ever done before, and Henry knew that for years she had nursed the grievance of Dominic's abrupt withdrawal from her life when he discovered her infidelity.

After dinner was over, Susan went up on deck. The skies had cleared, and a pale moon illuminated the scene with a silvery light. Across the water, the lights of the villas, many of which were floodlit at night, and the myriad lights of Monte Carlo along the coast gave the picture of a fairy-tale charm which Susan thought she would never forget. The sound of the waves, lapping softly beneath the yacht, soothed her nerves, and for a few moments she was at peace with herself.

Then she became aware of Dominic leaning with his back against the rail beside her, looking at her profile intently. She shivered. As always he made her completely aware of herself as a woman.

'What are you thinking?' he asked gently.

'Nothing in particular,' she answered. 'It's a wonderful night, isn't it?'

'Hmn. I guess so.' He sounded non-committal.

'What time do you leave in the morning?'

'About eleven, I guess. We'll have lunch at the airport in Nice and then we're boarding the flight for London. I have some business to attend to there before flying on to New York.'

'I see.'

'You only have about another ten days here, don't

you?' he said quietly. 'Then Jon is due back at school. When are you and Amanda leaving for the Bahamas?'

'Oh, I'm not sure. Not till later in the summer, I think. After all, my friend Delia is getting married later this year, and I'd like to be at her wedding.'

Dominic drew out his cigars and lit one broodingly, his eyes dark and passionate.

'Weddings,' he muttered. 'Marriages!' He bit his cigar savagely. 'I could kill Veronica at times like this! We're so helpless!'

'Don't talk about killing,' she whispered breathlessly. 'You don't really mean it.'

'Don't I? Perhaps not. But man is a primitive creature at best. At worst he's little more than an animal. Or is that an insult to the animal world? After all, animals don't do many of the things that man has been accused of.'

Susan sighed. 'I know. And I think talking like this is no good to either of us. There's nothing to say, nothing to be done!'

Dominic turned away, clenching his fists. 'You're right, of course. I'll go down to my cabin. I think I'll get good and drunk. Perhaps then I'll be able to rid myself of this . . . this . . . vengefulness!'

The night was long for Susan, too. She tossed about on her bunk until first light when she fell into a deep slumber and had to be awakened by the steward at nine-thirty.

She sprang out of bed, her head thudding sickeningly with an awful ache, and quickly poured herself a cup of black coffee from the percolator on the table beside the bed. Two aspirins eased the ache a little, but nothing could rouse the painful agony of the knowledge of Dominic's imminent departure. She wanted to run to him and beg him to take her with him, but she knew she could not, and that even if she did he would not do it. But what comfort would she get from her virginity as the years went by without the fulfilment of their love?

Dominic himself had eaten no breakfast but had fortified himself with several cups of coffee. He, too, had a headache from the amount of alcohol he had consumed the night before, and although he had experienced a few hours of oblivion, this morning he was back where he started from.

He was in his study, packing his brief-case, when there was a knock at the door, and after he had called 'Come' the steward entered.

'Well?' he said. 'What is it?'

'There's a gentleman to see you, sir,' said the steward respectfully. 'He says it's very urgent, and could you see him now. I told him you were getting ready to leave, but he said he was sure you would want to see him. He said his name was Harrison, sir. Arnold Harrison.'

Dominic put down his brief-case slowly. 'Are you sure that's the man's name?'

'Of course, sir. Will you see him, sir? Or shall I tell him you're too busy?'

'Oh, no, don't do that.' Dominic felt the palms of his hands grow moist. 'I'll see him, Parker. Yes, send him in. And, please, I don't want to be disturbed while this gentleman is here, do you understand?'

'Yes, sir.' The steward withdrew, and a few minutes later he returned with a tall, thin man wearing a dark moustache. He was dressed in a light fawn lounge suit, and was carrying a dark brown hat. Although Dominic had never seen him before, he recognized the type Veronica went for. The smart, rather too loud boys with the over-indulged air of hangers-on. What on earth she saw in these types, Dominic could never understand.

He came in, smiling rather ingratiatingly, and Dominic frowned, and waited until the steward had closed the door before speaking.

'Well?' he said, when the steward had gone. 'Why are you here? I imagine it's something to do with Veronica.'

'It is, yes.' Harrison nodded, and fingered the brim of his hat. 'May I sit down? I think what I have to say will be of interest to you.'

'Of course. Sit down.' Dominic was impatient, and seated himself on the edge of his desk, waiting for the other man to go on.

'You want a divorce from Veronica, is that right?'

'You know I do.'

'Precisely. Well, I am in a position to, as you might say, fulfil your desires.'

'Get to the point!' Dominic was sceptical, and yet a feeling of expectancy could not be entirely banished from his body. Was it possible that this man had persuaded her to change her mind?

'Veronica wants to marry me.' It was a statement of fact. 'At first I wasn't keen. Her allowance is not what you might call overly generous!'

'She gets two thousand a month.'

'Yes, but ... at today's prices ...' Harrison's voice trailed away. 'Anyway, to get on, you made some offer of a cash payment should she agree.'

'A hundred thousand,' agreed Dominic wearily. This was not happening! Surely no man could come to his mistress's husband with some kind of offer in this vein!

'Ah, yes. Quite a generous sum.' The man ran a tongue over his lips greedily. 'When Veronica contacted me again, that certainly helped to tip the scales in her favour ...'

'You're a swine,' muttered Dominic angrily.

'Maybe, but I'm what Veronica wants. I satisfy her, if you understand?'

Dominic wanted to throw him out. But something held him back.

'How do I know you're telling the truth?' asked Dominic.

'Ask Veronica!'

'Veronica!' Dominic was obviously amazed, and at that moment the door opened and Jon walked in.

'Dad! Can I see you for a minute? Oh, I didn't know you were busy . . .'

Dominic rose to his feet. 'Not now, Jon,' he said, frowning. 'I'm busy. I don't want to be disturbed. Come back in about fifteen minutes.'

Jon looked puzzled, and stared at Harrison. 'All right, Dad.' He looked back at his father, and then again at Harrison and shrugged. He went out quietly, closing the door, and Dominic compressed his lips. If this was going to come to anything, he wanted to keep Jon completely out of it.

'Carry on,' he said to Harrison now. 'You said Veronica. Is she here in Monte Carlo?'

'Yes. She's staying at the Cobana Palace Hotel. We booked in there last night.'

Dominic shook his head. 'But she was in the clinic three days ago. I saw her.'

'Can you imagine any clinic holding Veronica if she wanted to leave? She just walked out. Of course, she'll go back afterwards, but she thought you might not believe me, and she didn't want to risk this falling through.'

'What falling through? Come on, man. What is it you want?' Dominic stared at him. 'I can't believe it's as simple as you make it sound.'

'Veronica wants to marry me, right?'

'All right.'

'I'll marry Veronica; we'll give you the divorce without question. It all depends on you.'

'For God's sake, man.' Dominic was running out of

patience. 'Tell me what it is you want. I've already said I won't give Jon up . . .'

'Veronica doesn't want Jon!' Harrison's voice was scornful. 'If she told you that, she's a liar. Money is all that interests Veronica. She was only taking Jon to spite you.'

'I'm aware of that.'

'Good. Then how does half a million dollars strike you as a fair price?'

Harrison's manner had changed, and he now leaned forward in his chair, his eyes fixed on Dominic's face to see his reaction.

Dominic was staring at him, his eyes full of contempt.

'Do you mean to tell me that Veronica will divorce me for half a million dollars? Has she sunk that low?'

Harrison shifted uncomfortably. 'Come now, that's not the businesslike way to look at it. Veronica knows what she's giving and what she's asking. We merely thought the price could be better, that's all . . .'

'You mean you did!' Dominic's fist thumped down on the desk. 'I think she must have taken leave of her senses. What can she see in you?'

Harrison rose to his feet. 'I want no unpleasantness.' He sneered. 'Go and see Veronica if you don't believe me. She'll be only too happy to put you straight.' He coughed. 'And it occurs to me that should you refuse our request, we could make things pretty uncomfortable for you, publicity-wise. You've been staying here on the yacht with the girl you want to marry. I understand—'

'How can you know that?'

'We visited a club last night, and met a friend of yours, Carol Devereux.'

'Of course. Veronica's viper at her breast. She would enjoy the chance to put one over on me. However, Mr. Harrison,' Dominic's voice was sardonic, 'as money seems to be so important to Veronica, I hardly think she would jeopardize her future allowance by libelling me in any way. I have no need to pay her a penny and she knows it.'

'Perhaps you're right.' Harrison shrugged. 'It's a gamble I for one wouldn't care to take. However . . .' He looked at Dominic expectantly.

'I'll go see Veronica,' said Dominic slowly. 'But I'm promising nothing.' He moved to the door. 'Wait here. I won't be a moment.'

Outside the cabin, Dominic met Susan. Avoiding his eyes, she said:

'Have you seen Jon?'

Dominic frowned. 'About fifteen minutes ago. He came to the cabin to see me, but I was busy and sent him away – why?'

'He's disappeared. I've looked everywhere for him. I'd better ask Mac if he's seen him.'

'I'll come with you.' Dominic felt a twinge of concern. It was not like Jon to disappear for no apparent reason.

Mac had not seen him, but suggested that they ask some of the crew members who moved about the ship more freely than he did himself. A steward who served in the dining-saloon was summoned and he in turn questioned his fellow stewards. No one had seen Jon and Dominic felt really concerned.

A feeling of unease was beginning to bore into his brain. Was it possible that Jon had overheard some of their conversation, his and Harrison's, and learned that his mother was in Monte Carlo?

Taking Susan by the arm, Dominic led her to a quiet spot on the deck, and said:

'Veronica is in Monte Carlo. Do you think Jon could have gone to find her?'

Susan swallowed hard. This was not the time to ask questions about their association.

'Would he know where to look?' she asked quickly.

'Very likely,' said Dominic heavily. 'He may have overheard my conversation with Harrison.'

'I see. Well, I'm sure if he thought he could see her he would go. He was not satisfied, I think, with your visiting her recently, and not letting him know. Perhaps he thought there was something wrong.'

Dominic shook his head. 'Who knows?'

A steward came hurrying up to them. 'A dinghy has been taken from the stern,' he said. 'It's possible that Master Jon may have used that to reach the mainland.'

'Very possible,' agreed Dominic. 'Susan.' She looked up at him. 'Come with me. This concerns both of us.'

The Citroën was waiting for them when they reached the shore and Dominic took the wheel, with Susan beside him and Harrison in the back. He only hoped Jon had taken a bus into Monte Carlo. That way they should reach the hotel before he did. If he managed to get a taxi, they were too late. There were taxis for hire in Delice, but they had had no time to stop and ask whether one had been hired by a boy.

Dominic drove swiftly, the exotic scenery slipping by like the backcloth to the drama that was in the very air of the car. On the way, Dominic tried, as casually as he could, to explain the situation to Susan. She took little of it in. It did not seem possible that any man would want her sufficiently to sacrifice that amount of money to get his freedom to marry her. Just now, Jon was foremost in all their thoughts, and she wondered whether, if he did meet his mother, he would be terribly disappointed. She was not at all as he remembered her, that much was certain, and if she treated him badly it might distress him emotionally.

CHAPTER TWELVE

THE Cobana Palace was the kind of plushy hotel Susan had only read about. Its silver, blue and green décor was coolly luxurious, and the guests arriving and departing through its plate-glass doors were just as opulent.

Susan, in a simple white linen dress which revealed the slender lines of her figure and left most of her slender back bare, felt grossly under-dressed, and only Dominic in his dark suit melted easily into his surroundings. Harrison, for all his flashy style of dressing, looked nothing more than what he was.

Veronica and her boy-friend had taken a suite of rooms on the first floor, and as Harrison was already known to the bell-hop, they were delivered swiftly to the first floor where a silver-grey carpeted corridor led along to the suite.

Dominic strode ahead. He left the other two behind him. He had ascertained the number of the suite from Harrison and upon reaching the door he flung it open unceremoniously. As Jon turned a stricken face to him he knew he was too late to save him from finding out the truth, once and for all.

Susan, behind Dominic, pressed a hand to her stomach to try to prevent its churning, as Veronica, resplendent in a jade-green pyjama suit, rose to greet them. Gone were the grey streaks Dominic had seen at the clinic the other day. Her hair now shone glossily red, while her make-up today hid the lines of self-indulgence on her face.

'Dominic! How nice!' Her tone was honeyed, but her face grew a little bitter as her eyes rested on Susan's fair youthful beauty. 'And this must be Susan. How charming to meet you, my dear. So much better to be civilized about these things, don't you think?'

179

Susan allowed Veronica to shake her hand as though in a dream. This could just not be happening!

But it was. Veronica was quite businesslike. She turned to Dominic and said:

'Have you decided?'

'Never mind that,' said Dominic. 'What have you been saying to Jon?'

He was watching Jon as he stood behind his mother. Jon was watching Veronica in much the same way as the rabbit watches the snake, and Dominic felt the weight of his responsibilities for this boy. He knew he had done the right thing by taking him away from his mother all those years before. Veronica would have ruined his life; she had the kind of personality that could destroy anything it came into contact with.

'To Jon?' Veronica shrugged. 'Darling, Jon has got some mistaken idea that I actually wanted him to live with me!' She laughed. 'Jon darling, do I look the kind of homely person you need? I hope not.' Her eyes rested on Susan. 'Susan is much more in your line, darling, and if she marries your father, you'll make a happy threesome, won't you? Now, Dominic, have you decided?'

Dominic's shoulders hunched. Suddenly he wanted to get away. He felt he never wanted to see her again in his life. He had had enough. They had all had enough. He had come here hoping to persuade Veronica against marrying Harrison for her own good, but now it didn't seem to matter any longer. He had fooled himself all these years. They, Veronica and Harrison, were two of a kind. She would never change. She had been born that way, and he had been too young and too foolish and blinded by self-recriminations to see it before. Now it was all clear to him. Veronica could have her money, and her divorce. He would have Susan, and Veronica would have Harrison. They deserved each other. And Jon – well, Jon, he would be happier without ever knowing any more about his mother than he knew today. It would take him a long time to forget this day, but once he had he would see clearly again.

'All right, Veronica,' said Dominic quietly. 'You can have the money. I'll see about the agreement as soon as I get back to London. I'll have to have your signature for certain documents, but I suppose I can contact you at the clinic.'

Veronica smiled triumphantly at Harrison. 'Of course, darling. Will you stay and have a drink? Arnie darling . . .'

'Not for us,' said Dominic, taking Susan's arm in one hand, and Jon's in the other. 'We're leaving.'

'All rightie. Be seeing you.' Veronica smiled, and the last Susan saw of her was the jade-green pyjama suit as she flung herself exuberantly into Arnold Harrison's arms.

The journey back to the yacht began silently. Susan now sat in the back and Jon sat beside his father in the front. She wanted them to feel they could talk freely, and Dominic was grateful.

Jon spoke first, and when he did his voice was shaky. 'I deliberately listened to what you were saying,' he said, by way of an explanation. 'I heard my mother's name mentioned as I came into the room and I wanted to know what was going on. When I heard you say she'd asked for me, I wanted to see her, to find out for myself. I guess I was a silly fool, wasn't I?'

Dominic shrugged. 'Perhaps you did the right thing. If you'd never seen her you would never have known whether I was telling the whole truth or not, would you?' Jon shook his head. 'Did she tell you about Susan – and me?'

'Yes.' Jon buttoned his jacket and then unbuttoned it again, revealing clearly his feelings. 'I – I was surprised that you hadn't told me.'

Dominic sighed. 'I'll explain about that later. You can rest assured it's no grim secret. We just never thought it would happen.'

Jon nodded. 'Mother again, I suppose.'

'Yes. I'm afraid your mother has changed a lot since she had you.' Dominic shrugged. 'And about Susan, what did you think?'

Susan held her breath.

'I didn't mind exactly.' He looked a little shamefaced. 'I rather liked Susan myself. I guess she's a bit old for me, though.' He flushed, and impulsively Susan leaned forward and hugged him.

'Oh, Jon,' she whispered. 'We're going to have such good times together . . .'

It was almost exactly a year later that the Halstad family left their home in Wiltshire and journeyed to Monte Carlo in Dominic's private aircraft. They landed at a private landing field, and drove down to Delice in the same Citroën that Susan now regarded very favourably. After all, had not she and Dominic exchanged their first kiss in this car?

She glanced at Dominic as they drove along, and then glanced round at Jon in the back.

'Happy?' asked Dominic, his eyes gentle, his youthful expression indicative of the idyllic three months they had been married.

'Wonderfully,' exclaimed Susan, lying back in her seat, and pressing her fingers together. 'How long can we stay here?'

Dominic smiled. 'Well, I guess about six weeks, and then, when Jon returns to school, I have my resignation to the board to file and then we become the squires of Tipton Maryvale.' He chuckled. 'Are you sure that's what you want? Won't you miss the kind of social life we have in London?'

'Darling,' Susan's voice was soft, 'I married you because I loved you and wanted you all to myself. Not to share with the staff of the Halstad Press and every promiscuous female that comes along.'

Jon leaned forward. 'And in the holidays I intend to breed racehorses. Sammy the groom was telling me there's a mint of money to be made in that.'

Dominic grinned. 'Money! God, how sick I am of that word.'

'And me,' said Susan. 'Jon, honey, do you think you could race your horses just for fun?'

Jon smiled. 'I guess I could, Susan. But it's in the blood, you know. Money-making, I mean.'

Susan laughed. 'All right. Oh, I feel so happy, I could yell!'

Dominic looked down at her. 'And me,' he said.

Mills & Boon Classics

The very best of Mills & Boon
romances, brought back for those of you
who missed reading them when they
were first published.

There are three other Classics for you to collect this
September

NO FRIEND OF MINE
by Lilian Peake
Lester Kings was her brother's friend, not hers, Elise told herself
firmly. She had never liked him when she was a child, and now
he had come back into their lives the old antagonism was there
still, as strong as ever. Yet somehow she just couldn't stop
thinking about him . . .

SHADE OF THE PALMS
by Roberta Leigh
To Stephen Brandon, Julia was no more than Miss Watson, his
unflappable, highly efficient secretary. A dowdy woman wearing
unfashionable clothes, sensible shoes and spectacles, he would
have thought if he'd considered the matter at all. But he was to
discover that appearances can be deceptive and that there was a
totally unexpected side to Julia . . .

THE BRIDE OF ROMANO
by Rebecca Stratton
It was the charming Paolo Veronese who had got Storm the job
of governess to the little Gino in southern Italy, but it was Gino's
stern guardian, Alexei Romano, who caused her all the heart-
searching. She knew that in getting involved with Alexei she
would be utterly outclassed, but all the same . . .

If you have difficulty in obtaining any of these books through
your local paperback retailer, write to:

Mills & Boon Reader Service
P.O. Box 236, Thornton Road, Croydon, Surrey, CR9 3RU.

The Mills & Boon Rose is the Rose of Romance

Every month there are ten new titles to choose from — ten new stories about people falling in love, people you want to read about, people in exciting, far-away places. Choose Mills & Boon. It's your way of relaxing:

September's titles are:

WHERE THE WOLF LEADS by *Jane Arbor*
Everybody seemed to behave like sheep where Dracon Leloupblanc was concerned. And why, thought Tara Dryden indignantly, should she add herself to their number?

THE DARK OASIS by *Margaret Pargeter*
When Mrs Martin's son ran off with Kurt d'Estier's fiancée, she persuaded her secretary Maxine to go off to Morocco to try to pacify Kurt.

BAREFOOT BRIDE by *Dorothy Cork*
To save face when she found her fiancé strangely unwelcoming, Amy pretended that she was going to marry the cynical Mike Saunders instead — then Mike stunned her by taking her up on it . . .

A TOUCH OF THE DEVIL by *Anne Weale*
There was mutual attraction between Joe Crawford and Bianca — but marriage, Joe made it clear, was not in his mind.

THE SILVER THAW by *Betty Neels*
A holiday in Norway was supposed to give Amelia and her fiancé Tom a chance to get their affairs settled once and for all. But somehow she found herself seeing far more of Gideon van der Tolck.

DANGEROUS TIDE by *Elizabeth Graham*
Her ex-husband was the last person Toni had expected to meet on board a cruise ship to Mexico. But he, it appeared, had expected to meet her . . .

MARRIAGE IN HASTE by *Sue Peters*
Trapped in a Far Eastern country on the brink of civil war, Netta could only manage to escape if she married the mysterious Joss de Courcy . . .

THE TENDER LEAVES by *Essie Summers*
Searching for her father in New Zealand, Maria could have done without the help of the disapproving Struan Mandeville. But could she *really* do without Struan?

LOVE AND NO MARRIAGE by *Roberta Leigh*
Career woman Samantha swiftly fell in love with Bart Jackson, who had no time for career girls and thought she was a quiet little homebody . . .

THE ICE MAIDEN by *Sally Wentworth*
Just for an experiment, Gemma and her friends had computerised the highly eligible Paul Verignac, and Gemma was proceeding to turn herself into 'his kind of woman' . . .

If you have difficulty in obtaining any of these books from your local paperback retailer, write to:

Mills & Boon Reader Service
P.O. Box 236, Thornton Road, Croydon, Surrey, CR9 3RU.

Mills & Boon Classics

The very best of Mills & Boon
romances, brought back for those of you
who missed reading them when they
were first published.

In
October
we bring back the following four
great romantic titles.

NO QUARTER ASKED
by Janet Dailey

Stacy Adams was a rich girl who wanted to sample real life for
a change, so she courageously took herself off alone to Texas
for a while. It was obvious from the first that the arrogant
rancher Cord Harris, for some reason, disapproved of her — but
why should she care what he thought?

MIRANDA'S MARRIAGE
by Margery Hilton

Desperation forced Miranda to encamp for the night in Jason
Steele's office suite, but unfortunately he found her there, and
after the unholy wrath that resulted she never dreamed that a
few months later she would become his wife. For Jason was
reputed to be a rake where women were concerned. So what
chance of happiness had Miranda?

THE LIBRARY TREE
by Lilian Peake

Carolyn Lyle was the niece of a very influential man, and
nothing would convince her new boss, that iceberg Richard
Hindon, that she was nothing but a spoiled, pampered darling
who couldn't be got rid of fast enough! Had she even got time
to make him change his mind about her?

PALACE OF THE POMEGRANATE
by Violet Winspear

Life had not been an easy ride for Grace Wilde and she had
every reason to be distrustful of men. Then, in the Persian
desert, she fell into the hands of another man, Kharim Khan,
who was different from any other man she had met . . .

The Mills & Boon Rose is the Rose of Romance

Look for the Mills & Boon Rose next month

NO PASSING FANCY by *Kay Thorpe*
Claire's father had tricked her into going out to Tanzania, and there she found herself thrown into the company of the forceful Rod Gilvray.

HEART OF STONE by *Janet Dailey*
'I live hard and fast and love the same way,' declared Brock Canfield. At least Stephanie knew where she stood — but was what he offered enough for her?

WIFE BY CONTRACT by *Flora Kidd*
Her marriage to Damien Nikerios had brought Teri money and position — and the humiliation of knowing that Damien had only married her as a cover-up for his affair with his father's wife.

WHEN LIGHTNING STRIKES by *Jane Donnelly*
Robina had an abiding detestation of Leo Morgan who was responsible for so much of her unhappiness. And yet her life seemed to be inextricably involved with him ...

SHADOW OF DESIRE by *Sara Craven*
Ginny needed to keep Max Henrick at more than arm's length — which wasn't going to be easy when she was living and working in the same house.

FEAR OF LOVE by *Carole Mortimer*
If Alexandra wanted to marry Roger Young, that, she felt, was her own affair . Just what business was it of the high-handed Dominic Tempest?

WIFE FOR A YEAR by *Roberta Leigh*
Juliet had married Damon Masters to enable him to take an important job in one of the Gulf states. She had no feeling for him — or so she thought ...

THE WINDS OF WINTER by *Sandra Field*
Anne Metcalfe had assumed a new name and identity to return, after four years, to her husband's house. She just *had* to discover if what she suspected was true ...

FLAMINGO PARK by *Margaret Way*
What right did Nick Langford have to try and run Kendall's life for her? She was quite capable of looking after herself — wasn't she?

SWEET NOT ALWAYS by *Karen van der Zee*
Was Jacqueline's job in Ghana the real challenge, or was it Matt Simmons, her boss, who seemed so determined to think badly of her?

If you have difficulty in obtaining any of these books from your local paperback retailer, write to:

Mills & Boon Reader Service
P.O. Box 236, Thornton Road, Croydon, Surrey, CR9 3RU.

Available October 1980

Doctor Nurse Romances

and September's
stories of romantic relationships behind the scenes
of modern medical life are:

FIRST YEAR LOVE
by Clare Lavenham

When Kate started her nursing career at Northleigh
Hospital, she was thrilled to recognise the consultant
surgeon as a long-time friend of her brother's. Might her
childish hero-worship now blossom into something more
mature? Or was she looking in the wrong direction
altogether?

SURGEON IN CHARGE
(Winter of Change)
by Betty Neels

Mary Jane was over twenty-one, and a competent staff
nurse, so when she inherited a fortune she was furious
to find that she also had a guardian — the high-handed
Fabian van der Blocq. But what could she do about it
— or him?

Order your copies today from your local paperback retailer

Masquerade
Historical Romances

Intrigue excitement romance

CROMWELL'S CAPTAIN
by Anne Madden

Why should Cathie Gifford, who came of a staunchly
Royalist family, feel compelled to tend the wounded
Roundhead captain? And why should a man like
Piers Denham, who had betrayed his own kind by
fighting for Parliament, be able to shake her loyalty
to the King?

HOUSE OF SATAN
by Gina Veronese

Count Anton von Arnheim's Viennese mansion was
notorious, even in the pleasure-loving society of 1785.
And into it came Eloise, the Count's innocent and
beautiful ward. How long could she go on living
happily in the House of Satan?

**Look out for these titles in your local paperback shop from
12th September 1980**